Hellman
DOWNFALL

GERRY FINLEY-DAY • MIKE DOREY • PATRICK WRIGHT • JIM WATSON

HELLMAN OF HAMMER FORCE CREATED BY GERRY FINLEY-DAY AND MIKE DOREY

Hellman

AN INTRODUCTION

Tonight the sun goes down on more suffering than ever before in the world.

– Winston Churchill, February 1945

A STRANGE THING HAPPENS IN THIS SECOND COLLECTION OF HELLMAN, as the suddenly orphaned **Action** strip finds a natural home in the newly amalgamated **Battle Action**. At first it seems like business as usual, with the good-hearted Panzer commander going out of his way to fight what he deems to be a clean war - prisoners are taken, massacres are thwarted, chances are granted to honourable opponents. Writer Gerry Finley-Day employs his famous blend of high-octane action and quite startling contrivance, bending both historical fact and the laws of physics to his will as required. Then, suddenly, the story takes a sharp left turn into the pits of hell.

This is not to say that the book's opening episodes aren't worth reading; original *Hellman* artist Mike Dorey rejoins Finley-Day to take us back to basics, filling in the gaps of Hammer Force's service in Poland, France and the Balkans.

The late Jim Watson joins in with his unmistakable style. My own favourite among these stories is set on the plains of Thermopylae, with our hero's trademark gallantry being returned by an amusingly upper-class Englishman. Coincidentally, this episode sees the arrival of the superb Pat Wright, whose incredible level of detail makes him a worthy match for Dorey – indeed, the two will trade off on art duties from this point almost to the end of the series.

And then the Panzers strike east, and the German war machine finally bites off more than it can chew. Straightaway the tenor of the strip changes. In Russia there will be no fair play, no saving helpless enemies from burning tanks, no tending to the wounded under flags of truce. Nazi Fascism smashes full-tilt into Soviet Communism, two blind ogres tearing at each other's guts. Millions will die. Hellman and his men will be caught in the maelstrom, as over four long years the tables slowly turn - and the sins of Hitler's soldiers rebound on the people of Germany.

ALL SET, SIR ! HERE THEY COME – A WHOLE TANK COMPANY !
LIKE A MOB OF PEASANTS !

Things are bad enough initially, the road to Moscow being littered with portents of the doom to come. The excellent T-34 tank provides a nasty surprise for the overconfident Panzer crews, and the looming Russian winter - combined with an ever more capable Soviet defence - soon halts their progress towards the capital. Yet it is the savagery of Russian soldiers, in one brutal ambush after another, that provides the strongest contrast with earlier *Hellman* episodes. There are numerous accounts from the early war in the west of both sides treating each other with decency, albeit only as circumstances allowed (and leavened with occasional atrocity). Not here.

ut worse is to come. Once the story takes a three-
r leap to 1945, and Hellman - along with the rest
the German army - finds himself firmly in retreat,
true horror begins to reveal itself. The tanks may
bigger and better, but nothing can stop the massed
viet armies from steamrollering their way into the
herland - and as the defense crumbles, a ghastly
ch's brew of Russian vengeance and Nazi wrongdoing
lls out for all to see. There are slaughters of civilians
e, children included. There are death camps. There
traitors, and lynching parties, and - surely - there is
end of the Good German. That odd creation of '70s
tish war comics, designed to personify the point of
w of our opposition, has no part to play at the fall of
Third Reich.

AN EXTERMINATION CAMP... SO THEY EXIST! ALL THROUGH THE WAR WE HEARD RUMOURS BUT RECKONED IT WAS JUST ENEMY PROPAGANDA!
JA, IT'S TRUE!

AND SO WE'VE BEEN HELPING BUY TIME FOR BUTCHERY LIKE THIS! I THOUGHT THE SS WERE THE SORT OF RUNNING SORES EVERY ARMY OF EVERY COUNTRY HAS! BUT THIS — THIS IS A PURELY GERMAN DISEASE!

Or almost no part, for Kurt Hellman still has business to conclude. Clearly aware that such a nightmarish journey requires sympathetic traveling companions to get us through, Gerry Finley-Day provides an excellent cast - no great surprise from such a fine creator of characters. Hellman is joined by the enjoyably thuggish Max and Dekker, recruited some years before by the time-honoured methods of brutality and humiliation (the writer employed a similar device in *Dan Dare* around the same time, and it's pleasing to see both Commander Dare and Major Hellman enjoying such loyalty as a result). Also along for the ride are old reliable Sergeant Kessel, and the often ridiculous but occasionally lethal Heiler - the clue, with that one, being very much in the name.

Behind a wonderfully evocative cover (*The Fuhrer's funeral pyre awaits him...*) we find ourselves in Berlin for the Götterdämmerung. As the last Panther blasts its way towards Templehof airport and our hero faces his destiny in the ruins, we might pause to reflect on the achievement of *Hellman*. What we're given is a series of fascinating snapshots: generally, if not always in specific detail, a broadly accurate picture of the downfall of a nation, and what that means for its people once their crazed dictator abandons them to the inferno. Our guides are a vagabond tank crew, no less lost but fighting to the end. It's an interesting portrayal - in what was, after all, a 1978 boys' comic strip - of one of the most catastrophic moments in history. All credit to Gerry Finley-Day, Mike Dorey and Pat Wright, for what they managed to do.

Garth Ennis
April 2023

EACH WAR HAS TWO SIDES. . .AND EACH SIDE HAS ITS HEROES!
THE EARLY ADVENTURES OF...
HELLMAN OF HAMMER FORCE
BATTLE-ACTION
1ST SEPTEMBER, 1939 – AT FIRST LIGHT GERMANY UNLEASHES HER FORCES INTO NEIGHBOURING POLAND TO HERALD THE START OF WORLD WAR TWO SPEARHEADING THEM ARE THE BRAND NEW TANK DIVISIONS AND A BRAND NEW STYLE OF FIGHTING MAN. . . THE PANZER-MAN!
THE POLES WILL CRUMBLE BEFORE OUR WALL OF PANZER STEEL! NOTHING CAN STOP US!
MAJOR HUN'S PANZER FORCE WHEELED ON ACROSS THE POLISH PLAINS, UNTIL –
POLISH CAVALRY! A REGIMENT OF LANCERS TO TAKE ON THE PANZERS! THIS WILL BE A MASSACRE!
THE POLISH CAVALRY CHARGED INTO A WALL OF PANZER GUNS –
URRAA-AIEEEEE!
ON, HUN FORCE!
THE MASSACRE WAS SEEN BY HAUPTMANN KURT HELLMAN, IN ACTION AGAIN AFTER HE AND HIS CREW HAD FINISHED REPAIRS TO THEIR TANK'S ENGINE –
WE HAVE CAUGHT UP WITH HUN FORCE, SIR!
JA, BUT LOOK WHO THEY'RE FIGHTING. . . DEFENCELESS CAVALRY!
ORDERS CRACKLED INTO HELLMAN'S HEADPHONES. . . .
EVERY GUN IN HUN FORCE KEEP FIRING!
IGNORE THAT ORDER. . . WE'RE NOT TAKING PART IN A ONE-SIDED BLOODBATH!

LATER –
WUNDERBAR! THE WHOLE CAVALRY WAVE CUT TO BITS! THE LEFT-OVERS RAN LIKE RABBITS!
AND EVERY TANK SMOKING WITH THE HEAT OF OUR GUNS!
BUT –
ONE MOMENT, HELLMAN! THERE'S NO GUNSMOKE COMING FROM YOUR TANK! WHY?
NO, MAJOR HUN. BECAUSE –
SERGEANT KESSEL OF HELLMAN'S CREW SPOKE...
BECAUSE OUR GUNS COULDN'T FIRE, HERR MAJOR – THEY WERE JAMMED!
KESSEL'S COVERING UP FOR ME!
VERY WELL...BUT GUN MALFUNCTION IS AN OFFENCE! YOU ARE ALL ON A CHARGE!
THE TANK FORCE MADE BASE AT A CAVALRY BARRACKS HIT BY STUKAS –
WE'LL HAVE OUR OFFICERS' MESS IN THOSE STABLES!
BUT, LATER –
ON, COMRADES...THOSE PANZER SCUM KILLED OUR HORSES BUT WE STILL HOLD OUR LANCES!
INSIDE THE STABLES–
GUT – ALL MY OFFICERS ARE HERE BUT FOR HELLMAN. HIS PUNISHMENT IS BEING DUTY OFFICER WHILE HIS CREW SERVICE EVERY ONE OF OUR TANKS!
ACH – HE'LL NEVER BE ONE OF US. HERE'S TO HUN FORCE...
JA, TO –
DIE BY THE LANCE, GERMAN!
MEIN GOTT– POLES!
NEARBY WAS HELLMAN.
URGHHHH!
THAT NOISE FROM THE STABLES – SOUNDED LIKE A DEATH RATTLE!
DONNER! HUN AND THE OFFICERS WIPED OUT!
ONE MORE FOR THE SLAUGHTERHOUSE!
NO GUN, PANZER-MAN!

THEY'RE CLOSING IN FOR THE KILL! I'VE GOT ONE CHANCE!
HELLMAN LEAPT FOR THE MAN'S BACK–
TRY FOR THAT FORGE AND GRAB THE SMITH'S HAMMER!
URRA – HE'S MADE A CAVALRY LEAP!
NOW YOUR LANCES HAVE RUN INTO STRONGER STEEL!
NEXT MOMENT –
HOLD ON, SIR! WE'RE HERE!
KESSEL AND MY CREW!
RUN, CAVALRYMEN!
NOT BEFORE I NAIL THAT OFFICER...
THE HAMMER HITS FIRST, POLE!
AIEEE!
LATER –
WHAT HAPPENED HERE?
THE HUN FORCE OFFICERS WERE ALL WIPED OUT... ALL BUT HAUPTMANN HELLMAN HERE WHO FOUGHT IT OUT HAND-TO-HAND!
PANZER-GENERAL GUDERIAN HIMSELF!
HELLMAN, HEIN? AS OF NOW YOU ARE PROMOTED MAJOR AND IN COMMAND OF HUN FORCE BUT WITH HUN DEAD YOU WILL NEED A NEW NAME FOR YOUR PANZERS...
HAMMER FORCE WILL BE THE NAME WE FIGHT UNDER, GENERAL... BECAUSE MY FORCE WILL STRIKE SQUARELY LIKE THE HAMMER!

HAMMER INTO BATTLE WITH HELLMAN EVERY WEEK IN BATTLE-ACTION !

TANK ACTION WITH MAJOR KURT HELLMAN !

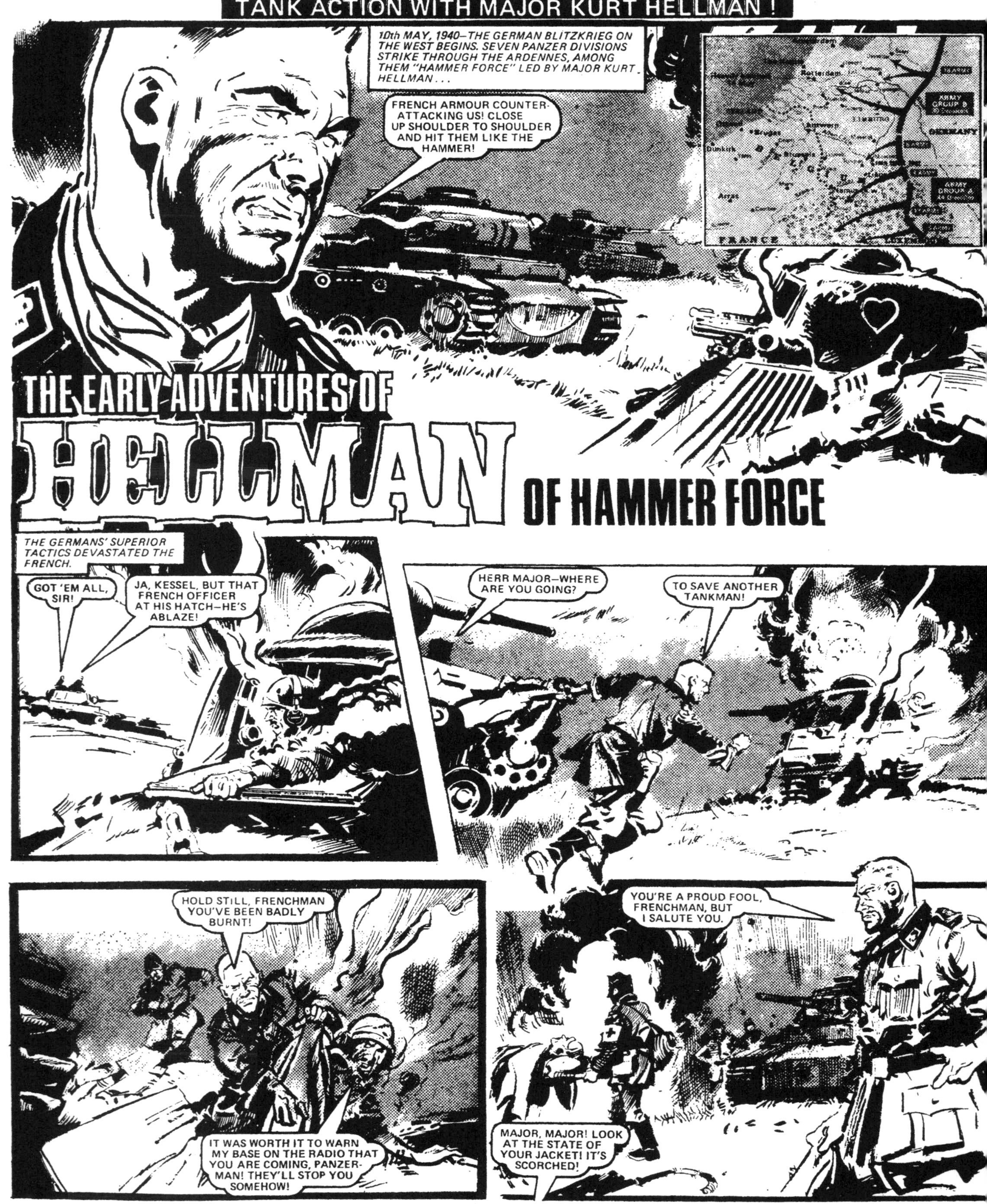

10th MAY, 1940—THE GERMAN BLITZKRIEG ON THE WEST BEGINS. SEVEN PANZER DIVISIONS STRIKE THROUGH THE ARDENNES, AMONG THEM "HAMMER FORCE" LED BY MAJOR KURT HELLMAN . . .
FRENCH ARMOUR COUNTER-ATTACKING US! CLOSE UP SHOULDER TO SHOULDER AND HIT THEM LIKE THE HAMMER!
Rotterdam
Dunkirk
Arras
GERMANY
FRANCE
THE EARLY ADVENTURES OF
HELLMAN
OF HAMMER FORCE
THE GERMANS' SUPERIOR TACTICS DEVASTATED THE FRENCH.
GOT 'EM ALL, SIR!
JA, KESSEL, BUT THAT FRENCH OFFICER AT HIS HATCH—HE'S ABLAZE!
HERR MAJOR—WHERE ARE YOU GOING?
TO SAVE ANOTHER TANKMAN!
HOLD STILL, FRENCHMAN YOU'VE BEEN BADLY BURNT!
IT WAS WORTH IT TO WARN MY BASE ON THE RADIO THAT YOU ARE COMING, PANZER-MAN! THEY'LL STOP YOU SOMEHOW!
YOU'RE A PROUD FOOL, FRENCHMAN, BUT I SALUTE YOU.
MAJOR, MAJOR! LOOK AT THE STATE OF YOUR JACKET! IT'S SCORCHED!

A SMALL GERMAN CORPORAL APPEARED–
HANS MULLER REPORTING, SIR. YOUR BATMAN.
FORGET THE JACKET, MULLER AND BOARD MY COMMAND TRAILER. HAMMER FORCE IS MOVING ON FOR THE RIVER MEUSE!
BUT AT THE LARGEST RIVER BETWEEN GERMANY AND THE CHANNEL, THE FRENCH WERE AT WORK!
BLAMM! WE'VE BLOWN THIS AND OTHER BRIDGES UP IN YOUR FACES, GERMANS!
AND–
AH, HELLMAN–NO GO HERE. WE'RE ALL STUCK THIS SIDE OF THE RIVER UNTIL OUR COMBAT ENGINEERS ARRIVE.
IMAGINE YOU TALKING TO A GENERAL AND LOOKING SO UNTIDY, SIR!
STOP FUSSING, MULLER! HAMMER FORCE IS GOING TO FIND A WAY ACROSS!
BUT WITH EVERY BRIDGE BLOWN HELLMAN WAS OUT OF LUCK THEN–
SIR! THAT MOUSE OF A BATMAN HAS JUMPED THE COLUMN!
WHAT THE DEVIL ARE YOU DOING NOW?
ACH, TRYING TO CLEAN YOUR UNIFORM, SIR. A PANZER MAJOR MUST ALWAYS LOOK HIS BEST!
FORGET IT, MOUSE–THE MAJOR HAS MORE IMPORTANT THINGS ON HIS MIND.
WAIT, LOOK AT ALL THESE CATTLE TRACKS LEADING INTO THE RIVER! THIS IS A FORD!
HERR MAJOR, YOUR SMART OFFICER'S TROUSERS!
QUIET, MULLER! THE FORD'S NOT VERY WIDE SO I'LL HAVE TO LEAD HAMMER FORCE ACROSS.
FIRST PANZER FOLLOW SLOWLY. ONE WRONG SWING AND IT'LL BE SWEPT AWAY!
HERE ARE THE PANZER GOGGLES YOU WANTED, SIR–

BUT FRENCH SOLDIERS WERE WATCHING.
GERMANS! CROSSING THE RIVER LIKE CATTLE!
AND THEY'LL DIE LIKE CATTLE– FAN OUT!
FRENCH SNIPERS ON THAT FAR BANK! THEY GOT WITTER!
AIEEEEEEE!
INSIDE, KESSEL WATCHED HELPLESSLY.
VERDAMMT FROGS! WE'RE TOO LOW IN THE WATER TO FIRE BACK!
THIS M.G. WILL HELP THE MAJOR!
MULLER! GOOD MAN!
IT'S MY TURN TO DO THE KILLING, FRENCH MEN!
ARGH!
FALL BACK! THE PIG'S MADE IT ACROSS!
HAMMER FORCE IS OVER! SIGNAL THE REST OF DIVISION, KESSEL.
DONE IT, SIR–THE GENERAL HIMSELF IS COMING STRAIGHT TO SEE YOU. BUT MULLER WON'T LIKE YOU LOOKING SO DIRTY!
AHEM! I HAVE THE MAJOR'S UNIFORM CLEANED AND READY TO WEAR, SERGEANT KESSEL!
MULLER! HE USED THAT PANZER ENGINE AS A STEAM PRESS! MAYBE HE'S NOT SUCH A MOUSE!
JA! GOOD WORK!
LATER–
MAJOR HELLMAN–THANK TO YOU OUR GROUP'S WELL INTO ENEMY LINES. I PROUDLY AWARD YOU THE IRON CROSS!
ALL CLEANED UP AND I'VE WO THIS MEDAL–NOT JUST FOR ME, BUT FOR ALL OF HAMMER FORCE! NEXT WE PUSH ON FOR THE COAST AND A LOT MORE CLEANING-UP TO DO!
HAMMER FORCE RACES FOR THE CHANNEL NEXT WEEK !

MAJOR KURT HELLMAN. . .KING OF THE PANZERS!
MAY, 1940–THE GERMAN BLITZKRIEG OF THE WEST IS ON WITH A VENGEANCE AS THEIR PANZERS RACE ACROSS THE PLAINS OF NORTH WEST EUROPE, ALL OUT FOR THE SEA. ONE FLYING COLUMN IS 'HAMMER FORCE', LED BY MAJOR KURT HELLMAN.
IT'LL TAKE MORE THAN A FEW SANDBAGS TO STOP US REACHING THE SEA–BUT THAT SIGN SHOWS THE BRITISH WON'T GIVE UP EASILY!
PANZERMEN WATCH OUT YOU STILL HAVE THE B.E.F. TO BEAT!
THE EARLY ADVENTURES OF
HELLMAN
OF HAMMER FORCE
SERGEANT KESSEL, DRIVER OF HELLMAN'S PANZER.
RUNNING LOW ON PETROL, SIR! WE NEED TO REFUEL!
OKAY, KESSEL–THERE'S ANOTHER PANZER FORCE COMING UP BEHIND.
ACH, THEY'RE WAFFEN S.S.–AND THEY'VE GOT TANK TRANSPORTERS!
THE LAZY NAZI PIGS ARE SAVING WEAR AND TEAR ON THEIR PANZERS SO THEY'LL HAVE PLENTY OF PETROL TO SPARE.
BUT–
YAAH!
OUT OF THE WAY, DOG SOLDIERS! YOU GET NOTHING FROM THE S.S.! WE'LL BE FIRST TO REACH THE SEA!
BUT AHEAD, BRITISH TROOPS WAITED–
S.S. HUH? THE SNAKES HAVE WALKED RIGHT INTO OUR TRAP. . .FIRE!

BRITISH AMBUSH! UNLOAD OUR PANZERS–SCHNELL!
NO USE, SNAKE–YOU CAN'T TOUCH A MATILDA'S PLATING! CLOSE IN LADS!
ON A RISE HELLMAN'S COMMAND TANK HAD ARRIVED–
BRITISH TRAP! A BEAUTY, TOO! I'M NO NAZI-LOVER, BUT I MUST HELP. TOP SPEED FORWARD, KESSEL!
BLAST OUT THE MATILDA'S TRACKS. THAT'S THE WAY TO BREAK UP THAT LINE!
FLANK ATTACK! LONE ARMY PANZER COMING IN FAST LIKE A CAVALRY SKIRMISHER!
AND–
WE'VE BROKEN UP THE BRITISH LINE–NOW THOSE S.S. SURVIVORS HAVE A WAY OUT OF THE TRAP!
QUICK! QUICK!
THEY'VE BROKEN OUT! NOW FOLLOW THEM FAST, KESSEL!
I CAN'T, MAJOR–THE ENGINE'S STALLING!
THERE'S LESS THAN SIXTY SECONDS OF FUEL LEFT–AND THE TOMMIES ARE COMING IN ON ALL SIDES!
ONE CHANCE–DRIVE DEAD AHEAD–UP ON TO THAT S.S. TANK TRANSPORTER!
JA, THE TRANSPORTER'S INTACT AND WE CAN MAKE IT–BUT WHO'LL DRIVE IT, MAJOR?
I WILL! BALING OUT NOW!
TUEFEL! TWO TOMMY SOLDIERS!
YOU JUST JUMPED INTO BIG TROUBLE, JERRY–STICK HIM!

NEIN! I CARRY PANZER PLATING AS A SHIELD, IT BREAKS EVEN BAYONET STEEL!
YAAAARGH!
DROPPED THEM! MUST GET TO THAT TRANSPORTER CAB!
MADE IT! NOW TO DRIVE LIKE A BAT OUT OF HELL!
BUT—
SAY THE WORD, SIR! I CAN'T MISS FROM HERE!
HOLD YOUR FIRE! THAT MADMAN ISN'T S.S.— HE'S ARMY TANKMAN LIKE US. HE DESERVES TO MAKE IT.
THANKS, BRITISH TANKMAN. . . I OWE YOU A GOOD TURN! MAYBE I'LL GET A CHANCE TO REPAY YOU ONE DAY.
HELLMAN RACED ON BACK TO HIS LINES AND THE FURIOUS S.S. MEN . . .
THOSE TOMMY SCUM WILL PAY FOR CUTTING UP MY COLUMN! I'VE CALLED IN A STUKA STRIKE!
STUKAS! THEN THE TOMMIES WILL SOON BE DEAD OR PRISONERS. MEANTIME, I THINK WE'VE EARNT THIS PETROL!
SOON—
BACK ON THE ROAD AGAIN! WE'VE LEFT THOSE S.S. STORMTROOPERS TO MOP UP AFTER THE STUKA ATTACKS!
SIR!—REPORT IN FROM THEM!
JA, HELLMAN. WE HAVE THE BRITISH TANKMEN ROUNDED UP AND THEY'LL PAY FOR THEIR AMBUSH. WE'RE GOING TO HAVE THEM SHOT!
AS THE WORDS DIED IN HIS RADIO—
HAMMER FORCE HALT! I'M NOT LETTING THOSE BRITISH BE BUTCHERED. . . WE'RE GOING BACK TO HELP THEM!
CAN HELLMAN PREVENT A MASSACRE? SEE THE DRAMATIC DEVELOPMENTS!

HELLMAN MAKES A BRAVE DECISION... BUT IT COULD COST HIM HIS LIFE!
THE EARLY ADVENTURES OF
HELLMAN
OF HAMMER FORCE
MAY, 1940 — MONTH OF THE GERMAN BLITZKRIEG ON NORTH-WEST EUROPE. FRONTING ONE ADVANCE HAVE BEEN THE PANZERS OF HAMMER FORCE. BUT NOW THEIR LEADER, MAJOR KURT HELLMAN, HAS CALLED A SUDDEN HALT!
TO HELL WITH THE RACE TO THE SEA — WE'RE TURNING BACK TO STOP A MASS MURDER OF BRITISH SOLDIERS!
BUT THE BRITISH ARE PRISONERS OF THE WAFFEN S.S. THE MAJOR'S SIGNING HIS OWN DEATH WARRANT!
AUVILLE
WAFFEN SS
DUNKERQUE
SOME MILES AWAY, THE WAFFEN S.S. REGIMENT HAD TAKEN OVER A FRENCH FARM WITH THEIR USUAL BRUTALITY —
GET OUT OF HERE, FROG! TAKE YOUR ONIONS AND GARLIC AND THINK YOURSELF LUCKY YOU'RE NOT IN THAT BARN WITH THE BRITISH!
INSIDE THE BARN —
THEM S.S. HAVE BEATEN UP THAT OLD FRENCHIE! DON'T RECKON MUCH ON OUR CHANCES, MATES!
WAIT — NEW ARRIVALS! IT'S THAT ARMY PANZER-MAN WHO BEAT US!
TURN THE TOMMY PRISONERS OVER TO ME! I WAS THE MAN WHO BEAT THEM AND I'VE RADIOED MY GENERAL FOR AUTHORITY!
ACH, MY DEAR MAJOR HELLMAN, CAN IT BE YOU ARE TRYING TO CROSS THE WAFFEN S.S.?
JUST THEN, HELLMAN'S DIVISIONAL COMMANDER CAME THROUGH —
HELLMAN, GET THE HELL OUT OF THERE! NOBODY TACKLES THE WAFFEN S.S.! IF THEY WANT TO BUTCHER P.O.W.s THEN NOBODY CAN STOP THEM!

HELLMAN WAS FORCED TO OBEY AND PULL OUT.
HA! RUN, HAMMER FORCE – AND DON'T DARE CROSS THE S.S. AGAIN!
BUT, FARTHER DOWN THE ROAD –
I'VE BEEN THINKING OF A PLAN AGAINST THE WAFFEN S.S. BUT I NEED THE CREW'S HELP, SERGEANT KESSEL!
WE ARE BEHIND YOU, MAJOR! WHAT'S THE PLAN?
I'M PLANNING TO DO A SWOP AND IT INVOLVES THAT FRENCH CIVILIAN AHEAD! HERE'S WHAT YOU DO. . .
AND –
COME ON, FROG – YOU'RE COMING FOR A RIDE!
MON DIEU!
DON'T WORRY, FRENCHMAN – IT'S A GOOD SWOP, MY SET OF WHEELS FOR YOURS!
GOOD LUCK, SIR!
SOON –
HA – SO MUCH FOR THAT TOUGH FIGHTER HELL-MAN AND HIS FORCE – THEY'VE VANISHED IN A CLOUD OF DUST!
NOW WE CAN START OUR FUN WITH THE TOMMIES IN THE BARN! HELLO –
WELL, WELL – IT'S OLD FROG BACK AGAIN!
WE'LL REALLY MAKE HIM JUMP THIS TIME!
PLEASE, M'SIEU – MY CYCLE HAS SOME TROUBLE. . .
CHAIN TROUBLE!
UUH!
THAT'S THE GUARDS SILENCED, NOW TO GATHER SOME OF THOSE EGGS!

WHEN THE S.S. OFFICERS CAME OUT –
AUS! OUT WITH THE PRISONERS! LET'S GET DOWN TO BUSINESS!
SPANDAUS SET UP BEHIND THE BARN, HERR GRUPPENFUHRER!
LOOKS LIKE THIS IS IT, LADS!
SUDDENLY –
GOTT! THAT OLD FROG WITH HIS ONIONS AND GARLIC!
HA! HE WANTS TO JOIN THAT TOMMY LINE! SO BE IT – HE CAN DIE, TOO!
HA, HA! COME ON, FROG!
BEAT IT, ONION JOHNNY! GET OUTTA HERE!
NO, M'SIEU. . .I'VE COME TO SHOW YOU MY SPECIAL PRODUCE. . .
SEE? I'VE MORE THAN ONIONS AND GARLIC WITH ME –
GRENADES! HE'S GOT A BUNCH OF GRENADES!
THE JOKING IS OVER! OPEN FIRE, GUNNERS!
NO, GERMAN – THE JOKE'S ON YOU! GIVE 'EM THE GRENADES, LADS!
AIEEEEEE!
QUICK – YOUR ONLY CHANCE IS TO RUN WHILE THEY ARE SHOCKED!
DUNNO WHO YOU ARE, BUT THANKS, MATE!
THAT EVENING –
OKAY, GET LOST, OUR FRENCH FRIEND – THE MAJOR'S BACK!
AND I FEEL MUCH CLEANER NOW, KESSEL!
BUT HELLMAN'S BATMAN WASN'T SO SURE. AS HE CLEANED HIS MASTER'S ARMY SHIRT LATER –
NO-ONE ELSE IN HAMMER FORCE KNOWS WHAT MY MAJOR'S BEEN UP TO! BUT I HOPE HE DOESN'T DO IT AGAIN. . .PANZER GREASE I DON'T MIND, BUT GARLIC AND ONIONS. . . WHEWW!
NEXT WEEK – HAMMER FORCE VERSUS THE FRENCH FOREIGN LEGION !

THERE ARE NO PASSENGERS IN HELLMAN'S POWERFUL 'HAMMER FORCE'!
KEEP MOVING FAST, MEN! ONLY ANOTHER HUNDRED MILES TO THE SEA AND HAMMER FORCE WILL HIT IT FIRST!
THE EARLY ADVENTURES OF...
HELLMAN OF HAMMER FORCE
MAY, 1940–MONTH OF THE MIGHTY GERMAN BLITZKRIEG ON THE WEST. THE PANZER COLUMNS RACE ALL OUT FOR THE CHANNEL WITHOUT A PAUSE–AND ONE OF THE LEADING UNITS IS 'HAMMER FORCE' – A PANZER UNIT LED BY MAJOR KURT HELLMAN.
LEUTNANT WITTER HAD ONLY JUST JOINED HAMMER FORCE–
ACH, ONLY THE TANKS IN HAMMER FORCE ARE REALLY IMPORTANT! THOSE LIGHT TRUCKS AND BIKES ARE PASSENGERS!
IS THAT SO, WITTER?
HELLMAN LEAPT ON TO WITTER'S TANK-
DON'T EVER THINK THAT, MAN! EVERY SOLDIER IN HAMMER FORCE IS IMPORTANT TO ME!
SIR–OUR LEAD SCOUT SERGEANT DORNER'S BACK!

AND, AS HELLMAN JOINED HIS OUTRIDER –
FRENCH STRONG-POINTS AHEAD, SIR – LOOK AT THE SIZE OF 'EM!
IT IS PART OF THE UNFINISHED MAGINOT LINE!
AND LOOK, SIR – COMING OUT OF THE GUN-SLITS – WHITE FLAGS! THE FROGS ARE SURRENDERING!
FOLLOW ME, SCOUTS! LET'S GO TAKE THEIR SURRENDER – WE'LL SHOW THAT KID LEUTNANT!
NO, SCOUTS – WAIT!
BUT INSIDE
GOOD, THE POOR BOCHE FOOL FELL FOR OUR LEGION TRICK!
OLDEST IN THE BOOK! LET HIM HAVE IT, LEGIONAIRES!
AIEEEEEE!
THE DIRTY FROGS! THEY'VE GUNNED SERGEANT DORNER DOWN!
THE FRENCH OFFICER SPOKE INTO HIS LOUDSPEAKER MICROPHONE –
COME ON, PIGS! THIS LINE IS HELD BY THE LEGION ETRANGERE! YOU KNOW WHAT THAT MEANS?
THE FRENCH FOREIGN LEGION. ONE OF THEIR UNITS IS IN THERE! AND THEY –
THEY NEVER SURRENDER! TO TAKE THOSE STRONG-POINTS WE'LL HAVE TO FIGHT TO THE FINISH!
IN MAY OF 1940 SOME OF THE TOUGHEST LEGION UNITS HAD BEEN BROUGHT FROM NORTH AFRICA TO MAN THE FRENCH DEFENCES
HAMMER FORCE IS OUTGUNNED BY THOSE PILLBOXES – WE'D NEVER GET CLOSE ENOUGH
LISTEN, SIR . . . ON THE HAMMER FORCE FREQUENCY . . . IT'S SERGEANT DORNER!

SIR – I'VE HAD IT BUT I STILL GOT SOME TIME. I CAN TAKE THAT BIG PILLBOX BUT I NEED HELP.
I WANT A—A PACK OF PRIMED TANK SHELLS!
I GET YOU, DORNER! OKAY, LEUTNANT WITTER AND MYSELF WILL BE DELIVERING THEM!
M-ME?
AND—
OKAY, WITTER—LET'S GO!
KEEP RUNNING—WE'VE NO TANK ARMOUR TO HIDE BEHIND NOW!
WE'RE HERE, DORNER—YOU SURE YOU'RE HIT BAD?
ONE-WAY TICKET, SIR—BUT I'LL SHOW YOU HOW A GOOD RIDER CAN HELP WHERE TANKS CAN'T!
COME ON, WHEELS—ONE LAST RIDE!
THE MOTORBIKE SERGEANT KICKED HIS POWERFUL 750 INTO LIFE—
TEUFEL—HE'S GOT HIS BIKE UP AND HE'S RIDING LIKE A BAT OUT OF HELL FOR THAT PILLBOX!
A BAT LOADED WITH A BUNCH OF SHELLS!

SALAUD! THAT MADMAN ON THE MOTORBIKE– OUR BIG GUNS ARE RANGED TOO HIGH TO HIT HIM!
MACHINE GUNS ON HIM! NAIL HIM!
YAHHHHHHH!
THEY GOT HIM!
NOT YET, WITTER. NOW WATCH THE BEST BIKE-RIDING YOU'LL EVER SEE!
TRICK I–I LEARNED ON THE MUNICH SPEEDWAY–
NON! HE'S SKIDDING RIGHT INTO US!...
HE DID IT! THE HERO TOOK OUT THAT PILLBOX!
JA. DORNER DUG A WAY IN FOR US. NOW TO CALL MY PANZER-GRENADIER DETACHMENT UP HERE FAST!
SIR–YOU'RE PUTTING ON STEEL HELMET AND ASSAULT PACK!
JA, WITTER–AND YOU'LL DO THE SAME. OUR TANKS ARE USELESS AGAINST THOSE STRONG-POINT GUNS BUT WE'VE GOT TO OVERRUN THEM SOMEHOW. I'VE GOT TO LEAD HAMMER FORCE AGAINST THE REST OF THE LEGION MADMEN IN THERE–AND WE'LL FIGHT THEM HAND-TO-HAND!
LOOKS LIKE A DEADLY FIGHT IS BREWING! DON'T MISS IT NEXT WEEK!

HELLMAN LEADS HAMMER FORCE AGAINST THE FRENCH FOREIGN LEGION !

THOSE STRONGPOINT GUNS HAVE STOPPED MY TANKS DEAD — NOW IT'S UP TO MY PANZER-GRENADIER SQUADS TO HIT THOSE FOREIGN LEGION HAND-TO-HAND! IT WILL BE A VICIOUS FIGHT!

THE EARLY ADVENTURES OF HELLMAN OF HAMMER FORCE

FRANCE, MAY, 1940. THE GERMAN BLITZKRIEG CARRIES ON TOWARDS THE CHANNEL, BY-PASSING HEAVY POINTS OF RESISTANCE WHEREVER POSSIBLE. BUT MAJOR KURT HELLMAN'S HAMMER FORCE HAS FOUND ITS WAY BARRED BY A SECTION OF THE MAGINOT LINE, MANNED BY DEADEY FIGHTERS OF THE FRENCH FOREIGN LEGION —

BON — HERE COME THE BOCHE!

AND STRAIGHT INTO OUR STAKE-TRAP! GET READY TO FALL BACK...

LOOK — THOSE LEGION SCUM ARE PULLING BACK! AFTER THEM!

NEIN! WAIT...

NEIN! NEIN!

STEEL SPIKES AND BAYONETS... LIKE STAKES!

MEIN GOTT!

ARAB-STYLE TRAP. THOSE LEGION DEVILS HAVE BROUGHT THEIR DIRTY TRICKS WITH THEM FROM AFRICA!

HELLMAN YELLED TO HIS SHAKEN SOLDIERS –
OKAY. . . HELMETS OFF AND TOSS THEM OVER THOSE STAKES. THEN WE LEAP IN AND MOVE ALONG THE TUNNELS!
SOON –
IT'S DARK AND AS QUIET AS THE BERLIN UNDERGROUND!
JA – AND WE MIGHT HAVE TO PAY A HEAVY PRICE FOR TRAVELLING IT!
SUDDENLY –
LIGHTS OUT, GERMANS!
NEXT SECOND –
AIEEEE!
GOTT! THE DEVILS ARE COMING FROM ALL SIDES IN THE DARK!
STAY PUT, GRENADIERS – THIS PANZER OFFICER CARRIES HIS TANKMAN'S TORCH WITH HIM!
THAT ONE – GET HIM!
NO, IT'S LIGHTS OUT FOR YOU, LEGION!
AIEEEE!
AFTER A VICIOUS CLOSE-QUARTER GUNFIGHT –
THE DEVILS ARE FALLING BACK INTO THE MAIN TUNNEL! GET AFTER THEM – DON'T GIVE THEM A CHANCE TO LAY ANOTHER AMBUSH!
WE'LL GIVE THEM ONE LAST TRICK – THE BIGGEST AND BEST!
KEEP THE PIGS BACK WHILE WE PREPARE THE FUSE!
OUI – IF WE ARE TO DIE THEN THE GERMANS WILL, TOO!
SALLE DE MUNITIONS
THEIR GUNFIRE IS MURDEROUS!
THEY ARE UP TO SOMETHING. . . I'M SURE OF IT!

HEY BOCHE, PIGS. . SEE THE LEGION'S LAST SURPRISE FOR YOU!
THE MADMEN HAVE LIT A FUSE TO THE MAIN MAGAZINE! THEY'LL TAKE US WITH THEM!
MOVE, YOU TWO. . . INTO THIS TROLLEY! IT WILL BE OUR UNDERGROUND PANZER!
PUSHING US OFF NOW, SIR!
GET THEM! GET THEM!
SORRY, HARDMEN. . . BULLETS SPANG OFF A STEEL HIDE!
OUT AND FIGHT YOUR WAY TO THAT FUSE! GOT TO STOP THAT AMMO IN THERE GOING UP OR WE'RE ALL DEAD!
STEP OVER HERE, AND I'LL TAKE YOUR HEAD OFF, PIG!
YAHHHHHH!
HAVE MY STEEL HELMET INSTEAD!
AIEEEEEE!
AND THE LEGIONAIRE'S SCIMITAR SAVES US!
SOON THE STRONGPOINT SYSTEM HAD BEEN OVERRUN FROM WITHIN AND HELLMAN'S TANKS COULD ADVANCE AGAIN –
NOW THE WAY IS CLEAR TO THE COAST AND HAMMER FORCE IS IN THE RACE TO REACH IT FIRST!

NEXT WEEK – THE CHANNEL IS REACHED ... AND ENGLAND IS IN SIGHT !

RACE FOR THE CHANNEL WITH MAJOR KURT HELLMAN !

MAY, 1940 – THE GERMAN RACE TO THE CHANNEL REACHES ITS LAST LAP. AMONG THE ARMOURED UNITS ADVANCING ON THE COASTAL TOWNS IS HAMMER FORCE LED BY PANZER MAJOR KURT HELLMAN. . .

THE SEA AT LAST, MAJOR HELLMAN – THAT'S DUVILLE, A BIG FRENCH CASINO TOWN!

OUR TWO TANKS WILL DO A QUICK RECCE OF ITS STREETS!

THE EARLY ADVENTURES OF... HELLMAN OF HAMMER FORCE

I SMELL ENEMY TROOPS ! KEEP YOUR EYES PEELED!

LET THE LEAD TANK PASS! HE'LL BE TRAPPED LIKE A RAT WHEN WE BLAST THE SECOND PANZER!

AND –
CASINO
MEIN GOTT – FRENCH AMBUSH AND THEY'VE BLASTED WITTER!

HELLMAN SLAMMED HIS HATCH SHUT –
THE FRENCH ARE MASSED IN THE CASINO, SIR!
WE'RE WEARING PANZER STEEL, KESSEL – THAT'LL GET US IN! GO FOR ITS DOORS!

MON DIEU! THE MONSTER POWERS IN!

AIEEEE!
YOUR LUCK RAN OUT IN HERE, FRENCHMEN! SURRENDER OR ELSE!
SOON THE REST OF HAMMER FORCE HAD OVERRUN OTHER RESISTANCE IN THE TOWN –
WE DID IT, SIR—NOW OUR UNIT CAN HEAD FOR THE BEACH AND BE FIRST TO TOUCH THE WATER!
BUT SUDDENLY, OVER HELLMAN'S RADIO–
ALL WEHRMACHT UNITS STAND DOWN! TOTENKOPF AND LIEBSTANDARTE TO BE ALLOWED TO REACH THE SEA FIRST FOR PROPAGANDA!
ACH! HITLER'S PET DIVISIONS STEAL MY MEN'S GLORY!
THE LIEBSTANDARTE TANKS ROLLED ONTO THE SAND–
CAMERAMAN—START FILMING OUR LAST HUNDRED YARDS TO THE SEA!
JA, IT'S SAFE... NOTHING BUT OLD SHIP WRECKS OUT THERE SUNK BY STUKAS!
BUT HIDDEN BEHIND ONE WRECK –
JUST WHAT WE'VE BEEN WATCHING THE BEACH FOR-THE FIRST JERRY PANZERS! INTO THE OPEN – AND EVERY GUN BLAST THEM!
MEIN GOTT! A BRITISH CORVETTE AND ITS GUNS ARE RANGED ON US!
GOTT! ALL SIX TANKS SHOT TO BLAZES – BEFORE THEY COULD REACH THE SEA!
HELLMAN HAD RACED TO THE SEAFRONT.
BACK INTO HIDING SHE GOES – AND FROM THE BEACH THE RANGE IS TOO GREAT FOR OUR TANKS! WE HAVE TO GET INTO THE SEA TO GET THE RANGE...

. . . AND THOSE BATHING HUTS HAVE GIVEN ME AN IDEA! TELL HAMMER FORCE TO PREPARE FOR ACTION!
LATER, ON THE CORVETTE–
SIR–ON THAT BEACH! ANOTHER PANZER COMING!
ANYTHING ELSE TO BE SEEN, LOOKOUT?
NOTHING ELSE, SIR – ONLY SOME OLD BATHIN' HUTS!
OKAY–OUT INTO THE OPEN AND FINISH THIS ONE FAST!
SIR–SOMETHING'S WRONG! THEM BEACH HUTS EITHER SIDE–THEY'RE MOVING!
WHAT THE DEVIL'S GOING ON?
IT'S PANZERS! PANZERS BEHIND PUSHING THEM!
AND WITH THE HUTS AS CAMOUFLAGE WE'VE REACHED THE WATER! ANOTHER FIVE YARDS AND OUR GUNS WILL GET THEIR RANGE!
NOW. . . OPEN FIRE! AIM AT THE SHIP'S WATERLINE!
DAMMIT, GUNCREWS– GET THOSE PANZERS!
IT'S NO GOOD, SIR – THEY BEAT US TO IT! WE'RE HOLED AN' TAKING IN WATER!
ABANDON SHIP! MAKE FOR THE SHORE!
LATER–
PREPARE TO PICK UP SURVIVORS! HAMMER FORCE HAD THE LUCK TO REACH THE SEA FIRST! BUT LET'S HOPE OUR WINNING STREAK LASTS NEXT TIME WE ROLL OUR WHEELS INTO BATTLE!

MORE ACTION WITH HELLMAN NEXT WEEK !

BIG, BIG ACTION WITH TANK MAJOR KURT HELLMAN !
ARLY SPRING,1941–ALMOST A YEAR AFTER THE ERMAN BLITZKRIEGS ON THE CHANNEL, AND NOW NEW ONE IS ABOUT TO BE LAUNCHED–THIS TIME N THE SOUTH. IN THE GERMAN ALPS, THE ATTACK ORCES PREPARE–AMONG THEM 'HAMMER FORCE', TOUGH PANZER COLUMN LED BY MAJOR KURT ELLMAN.
CHECK YOUR PANZERS WELL, MEN! SOON WE MOVE INTO TOUGH MOUNTAIN COUNTRY!
THE EARLY ADVENTURES OF...
Hellman
OF HAMMER FORCE
AND EVERYONE KNOWS IT'S THE BALKANS WE'LL BE BLITZING!
OVE, ANOTHER GERMAN GIMENT WATCHED MMER FORCE–
WELL, WELL... IT IS THE PANZER HEROES OF FRANCE!
BUT IN THIS TERRAIN IT WILL BE US MOUNTAIN MEN WHO'LL GET THE GLORY. UNPACK THE ROPES–LET'S GIVE THOSE TANKMEN A FRIGHT!
AAAAH! ROPES LASSOING US!
GEBIRGSJAGER–MOUNTAIN TROOPS! TRYING TO RUB OUR FACES IN THE DIRT!
OKAY, SERGEANT KESSEL... LET'S SHOW THEM HOW HAMMER FORCE ACTS FAST IN DANGER! SMOKE SHELLS READY...
YES, MAJOR!
GOTT! SMOKE SHELL... CHOKING!
C-CAN'T SEE!

NOW, HAMMER FORCE—PULL HARD WHILE THEY'RE OFF BALANCE!
AAAAARGH!
OKAY, PANZERMEN. . .NOW WE'LL TEACH YOU A REAL MOUNTAIN LESSON . . .
JA, OUT WITH THE CLIMBING HAMMERS!
NO MORE, GEBIRGSJAGER! PUT DOWN THOSE HAMMERS!
SHUT IT, TANKMAN!
SUDDENLY, HELLMAN GRABBED HIS BLACKSMITH'S SLEDGEHAMMER, TAKEN FROM A POLISH STABLE AND NOW HIS UNIT'S SYMBOL—
I GAVE YOU AN ORDER! PUT DOWN THOSE HAMMERS . . .
WOW—LOOK AT THE MAJOR SWING!
MAJOR? YOU ARE AN OFFICER . . ?
JA—AND I'M A BAVARIAN, TOO. . . FROM THE MOUNTAINS. NOW, FORGET OUR DIFFERENCES AND HAVE A DRINK FROM MY STOCK OF ALPINE LAGER!
WE THOUGHT YOUR MAJOR WAS JUST A COMMON MECHANIC, WHAT TYPE OF SOLDIER IS HE?
A REAL PROFESSIONAL, MOUNTAIN MAN—YOU'LL SEE!

ESS THAN A MONTH LATER HE BLITZKRIEG STARTED— PERATION 'MARITA', THE NVASION OF GREECE—
FORWARD, HAMMER FORCE! GERMANY MUST SECURE ITS SOUTHERN FLANK IN EUROPE!
SOON—
THOSE MOUNTAINS AHEAD ARE THE 'GHOST' MOUNTAINS WITH A VITAL PASS LEADING TO THE PLAINS OF GREECE. WE'VE GOT TO TAKE THE PASS!
YOU TAKE THE LOW ROAD AND WE'LL TAKE THE HEIGHTS, HERR MAJOR! SEE YOU THERE!
THE GEBIRGSJAGER MOVED OFF INTO THE HEIGHTS—
GOOD LUCK, MOUNTAIN MEN! LET'S HOPE NOBODY'S WAITING FOR US IN THE PASS!
ON—
PROCEED WITH CAUTION! THESE HAIRPIN BENDS ARE EXTREMELY DANGEROUS!
AND, LATER—
THERE IT IS – THE GHOST PASS – SO CALLED BECAUSE MANY ARMIES INVADING GREECE WERE WIPED OUT HERE.
DDENLY—
GOTT—AN EXPLOSION UP THERE!
LEAD SCOUTS GET BACK! GET BACK!
AIEEEEEEEEEEE!

GOTT! PANZER THREE AND OUR SCOUT TEAM CRUSHED! BUT THE MOUNTAIN TROOPS SHOULD HAVE BEEN COVERING US!

HIGH ABOVE—

HEY, GERMANJA! YOU LIKE OUR WELCOME? INVADERS ALWAYS GET WELCOME IN THE GHOST MOUNTAINS!

WHO ARE THEY?

GREEK IRREGULARS . . . THEY'RE MOUNTAIN MEN, TOO.

AND THAT'S WHAT HAPPENED TO OUR GEBIRGS! THEY WERE AMBUSHED BY MEN WHO KNEW THESE GHOST MOUNTAINS!

HEY, GERMANJA—WE GO NOW! BUT YOU ARE SEALED UP WITH YOUR TANKS—YOU WILL COME NO FURTHER THROUGH THE GHOST MOUNTAINS!
THEY'RE RIGHT, DAMN THEM—WE'RE SEALED IN TIGHT!
WRONG, KESSEL—THESE KILLERS HAVEN'T STOPPED US—WE'RE GOING ON THROUGH!
THE MAJOR MUST HAVE AN IDEA . . BUT WHAT? HOW CAN HAMMER FORCE PASS THROUGH THE GHOST MOUNTAINS?

FIND OUT HOW IN NEXT WEEK'S EXPLOSIVE INSTALMENT !

HAMMER FORCE IS STRANDED – BUT HELLMAN SEES A WAY OUT !

APRIL, 1941. OPERATION MARITA, THE GERMAN ATTACK ON GREECE, IS UNDERWAY – BUT THIS TIME THE PANZERS ARE FINDING THE GOING VERY TOUGH. IN THE REGION KNOWN AS THE 'GHOST' MOUNTAINS, MAJOR KURT HELLMAN'S 'HAMMER FORCE' HAS BEEN STOPPED DEAD!

THE GREEKS MURDERED OUR MOUNTAIN TROOPERS – HUNG 'EM DEAD BY THEIR CLIMBIN' HOOKS!

THEN THEY AMBUSHED US AND SEALED UP THE PASS IN OUR FACES – WE'LL BE NEXT FOR THE CHOP!

THE EARLY ADVENTURES OF...

Hellman OF HAMMER FORCE

NO WE WON'T – WE'RE GOING TO TAKE THE BATTLE TO THEM!

OVER THAT MOUNTAIN? A COLUMN OF PANZERS? THE MAJOR'S HAD TOO MUCH THIN MOUNTAIN AIR!
AND NOW HE'S STARTED CLIMBING!

SOON –
THE BODIES OF OUR MOUNTAIN TROOPS! I'M NOT FAR FROM THE TOP...

BUT ONE GREEK IRREGULAR FIGHTER HAD STAYED BEHIND.
HAI-ANOTHER GERMAN COME TO JOIN THE GHOSTS!
DIE!
HIMMEL! I'M A DEAD MAN... UNLESS!
A CLIMBING SPIKE—USED FOR CUTTING INTO MOUNTAIN ROCK...
YAIEEEEEEEE!
BUT IT CAN ALSO CUT INTO MEN — THE AMBUSH IS STARTING TO BE AVENGED!
THE TOP... AND THE OTHER GREEK KILLERS HAVE GONE ALONG THAT RIDGE... LEAVING A CARELESS TRAIL. THEY THINK US TANKMEN ARE NO USE IN HIGH MOUNTAINS...
BUT THEY'LL HEAR FROM US AGAIN-TONIGHT! FIRST I PLAY THIS LIFTING CHAIN DOWN TO HAMMER FORCE.
THAT NIGHT, AT THE GREEK IRREGULARS' HIDEOUT IN THE 'GHOST MOUNTAINS' —
SOON WE DESCEND ON THOSE GERMANS BOTTLED UP IN THE PASS WITH THEIR PANZERS AND FINISH THEM!

WE'RE NO LONGER IN THE PASS, GREEK! START UP, HAMMER FORCE!
GERMAN VOICE, AND LISTEN – THAT ROAR ALL AROUND US!
ENGINES! THE ROAR OF ENGINES – AND LOOK!
HEADLIGHTS! TANK HEADLIGHTS! WE ARE SURROUNDED BY–BY PANZERS!
PANZERS – HERE? THOUSANDS OF FEET ABOVE ANY ROAD? IMPOSSIBLE!
IT'S TRUE, GREEKS! AND IF YOU DON'T DROP YOUR WEAPONS YOU'LL BE ABLE TO FEEL THEM!
YES! YES! KEEP YOUR PANZERS OFF!
NOW COME FORWARD, HANDS ON HEADS!
BUT–BUT I DO NOT UNDERSTAND. WHERE ARE THE TANKS? WE CANNOT SEE THEM! YET WE HEARD THEM!
WHAT YOU HEARD WAS CORRECT... PANZER ENGINES. ENGINES ARE THE ONLY THINGS WE BROUGHT, NOTHING MORE...
UH?
ACH ENGINE WAS TAKEN OUT F ITS PANZER AND HOISTED UP INTO THE HEIGHTS."
"THEN ONE WAS LOADED ON TO A RUNNING BOARD AND PULLED ACROSS THE MOUNTAIN RANGE BY ME AND MY CREWMEN, WORKING LIKE PACK MULES AND FOLLOWING THE TRAIL TO YOUR CAMP."

WE SITED THEM ROUND YOUR CAMP AND SWITCHED THEM ON! WE BLUFFED YOU IN THESE GHOST MOUNTAINS WITH GHOST TANKS!
THE FILTH —GO FOR HIM!
WE'LL MAKE A GHOST OF YOU, GERMAN MAJOR!
ANOTHER SECOND AND THEY'LL SLIT MY THROAT!
UNLESS!
AIEEEEEE!
THE MAJOR BROKE THE CHOCKS ON ONE OF THE ENGINES AND IT'S SWEPT THEM OVER THE EDGE !
BACK AT THE GHOST PASS –
OUR ENGINEERS ARE BLASTING A WAY THROUGH THE PASS FOR US, SIR.
JA, WE'LL REFIT OUR ENGINES AND SOON WE'LL BE RACING REDHOT ALL THE WAY SOUTH TO ATHENS. HAMMER FORCE HAS COME THROUGH THE GHOST MOUNTAINS ALIVE!
AN ENGLISH LORD PLOTS HELLMAN'S DOWNFALL NEXT ISSUE !

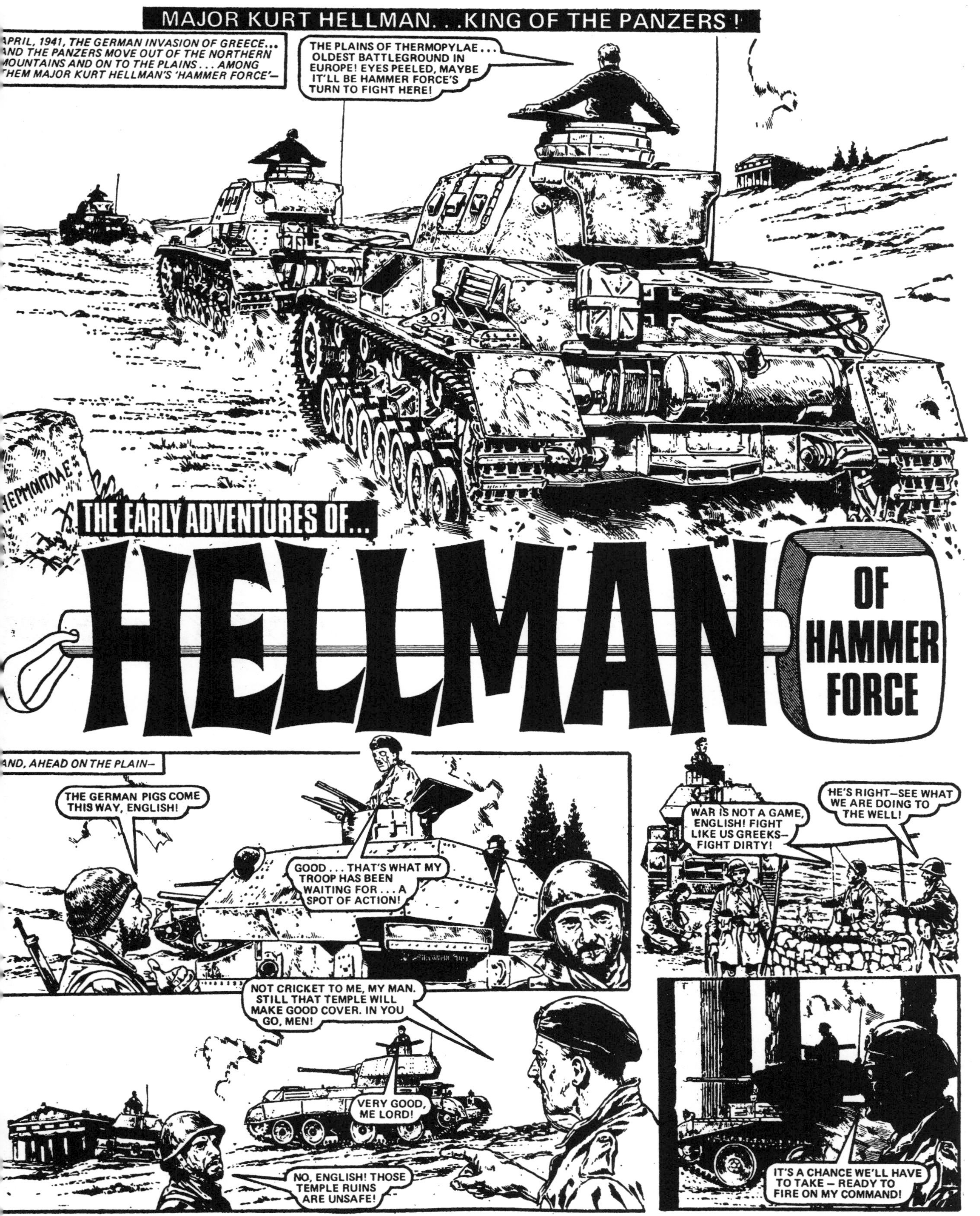
MAJOR KURT HELLMAN. . .KING OF THE PANZERS!
APRIL, 1941, THE GERMAN INVASION OF GREECE... AND THE PANZERS MOVE OUT OF THE NORTHERN MOUNTAINS AND ON TO THE PLAINS . . . AMONG THEM MAJOR KURT HELLMAN'S 'HAMMER FORCE'—
THE PLAINS OF THERMOPYLAE . . . OLDEST BATTLEGROUND IN EUROPE! EYES PEELED, MAYBE IT'LL BE HAMMER FORCE'S TURN TO FIGHT HERE!
THE EARLY ADVENTURES OF...
HELLMAN
OF HAMMER FORCE
AND, AHEAD ON THE PLAIN—
THE GERMAN PIGS COME THIS WAY, ENGLISH!
GOOD . . . THAT'S WHAT MY TROOP HAS BEEN WAITING FOR . . . A SPOT OF ACTION!
WAR IS NOT A GAME, ENGLISH! FIGHT LIKE US GREEKS— FIGHT DIRTY!
HE'S RIGHT—SEE WHAT WE ARE DOING TO THE WELL!
NOT CRICKET TO ME, MY MAN. STILL THAT TEMPLE WILL MAKE GOOD COVER. IN YOU GO, MEN!
VERY GOOD, ME LORD!
NO, ENGLISH! THOSE TEMPLE RUINS ARE UNSAFE!
IT'S A CHANCE WE'LL HAVE TO TAKE — READY TO FIRE ON MY COMMAND!

SOON, HELLMAN'S TANK PLATOON CAME INTO VIEW–
NOTHING TO BE SEEN ON THE PLAIN EXCEPT OLD TEMPLE RUINS, BUT PROCEED WITH CAUTION !
OKAY, CHAPS–START POTTING!
YAHHHHHH!
TEUFEL–TANK TRAP! BRITISH TANKS UNDER THAT TEMPLE ROOF!
BALE OUT! BALE OUT!
LET THEM RUN! NO MAN WILL SHOOT DOWN ANY OF THEM . . . IT'S BAD SPORTSMANSHIP!
BUT NOTHING WRONG WITH BAGGING THAT LAST PANZER! ALL GUNS ON HIM, CHAPS!
THEY'RE AFTER US NOW, SIR– AND THEY'VE GOT THE VANTAGE POINT IN THAT TEMPLE!
GET IN BEHIND THAT HIT PANZER!
WE'RE SAFE FOR THE MOMENT! BUT WHAT NOW?
LOOK, KESSEL–TO THE ROOF OF THE TEMPLE!

IT'S STARTING TO CRACK UP!
THE TANK BLASTS HAVE WEAKENED IT! NOW IT IS THE TOMMIES WHO WILL BE IN A TRAP!
S'TRUTH! THE ROOF'S COMING DOWN!
MOVE FAST, MAN. . . CLOSE ALL HATCHES!
MASONRY AND PILLARS TOPPLED OVER THE HELPLESS BRITISH TANKS.
TWO OF THE TANKS COMPLETELY DESTROYED AND THE OTHER IS STUCK . . . WAITING FOR THE REST OF THE ROOF TO ENTOMB IT! FORWARD, KESSEL – SCHNELL !
BUT THE WHOLE TEMPLE WILL COLLAPSE ANY SECOND!
THOSE TOMMIES DIDN'T TOUCH OUR MEN WHEN THEY BALED OUT–SO WE WON'T LET DECENT MEN DIE!
DRIVE ALONGSIDE THE TOMMY TANK–MOVE!
OPEN UP IN THERE, TOMMY–OPEN YOUR SIDEHATCH!

BY GAD—A GERMAN!
QUICKLY . . . YOU AND YOUR CREW CRAWL THROUGH INTO OUR PANZER—IT'S YOUR ONLY HOPE!
AND—
COME ON! FASTER!
YES, DO HURRY UP, CORPORAL, THERE'S A GOOD MAN!
MOMENTS LATER—
THERE IT GOES—NOW HIT REVERSE, KESSEL. WE'RE GOING TO MAKE IT!
HELLMAN'S TANK HALTED BY THE WELL—
DONNER!
YOU ARE NOW MY PRISONER. DISARM HIM, SERGEANT KESSEL!
DON'T DRINK THE WATER, MAJOR!
BEFORE YOU SHOOT ME, TAKE A LOOK AT THAT WELL WATER . . .
A FEW SPRIGS OF HERB FLOATING IN IT . . .
MEIN GOTT. . .HEMLOCK! THE FAMOUS POISON OF ANCIENT GREECE. THIS WELL WAS A DEATH-TRAP!
I SAW MY GREEK FRIENDS PREPARING IT FOR YOU. NOW I'VE REPAYED YOU FOR SAVING US!
THANKS, BRITISHER—ONE CLEAN MOMENT IN A DIRTY WAR. BUT MORE OF YOUR COMRADES WILL BE WAITING IN THE BATTLES AHEAD. . . SO I HOPE LUCK KEEPS WITH US IN THE KILLING-GROUNDS OF GREECE!

MORE ACTION WITH HELLMAN NEXT WEEK ! DON'T MISS HIM !

BLAZING BATTLE-ACTION WITH TANK MAJOR KURT HELLMAN !
THE EARLY ADVENTURES OF...
HELLMAN OF HAMMER FORCE
APRIL, 1941 – THE GERMAN ATTACK ON GREECE PUSHES SOUTH AND NOW OUT OF THE MOUNTAINS AND PLAINS THE PANZERS HEAD FOR THE COAST. AMONG THEM IS MAJOR KURT HELLMAN'S 'HAMMER FORCE' – AND NOW HE HAS PUSHED AHEAD WITH HIS PANZER GRENADIERS TO SPY OUT THEIR NEXT OBJECTIVE...
THAT WALLED TOWN AHEAD HAS TO BE TAKEN... SO LET'S HOPE IT'S NOT TOO WELL DEFENDED!
INSIDE HELLMAN'S TANK –
AAH – WE'RE ALMOST AT THE AEGEAN SEA AND I'VE BROUGHT MY SNORKEL ALONG FOR UNDERWATER SWIMMING!
BUT FIRST WE HAVE TO TAKE THE TOWN, WAGNER!
BUT MANNING THE WALLS OF THE GREEK TOWN WERE SEASONED ANZAC SOLDIERS OF THE BRITISH EXPEDITIONARY FORCE IN GREECE –
THIS LOT HAVE GOT A HAMMER FOR A BADGE, BUT THEY'LL BE THE ONES WHO GET HAMMERED!
LET FLY, FELLAS!
HELLMAN'S SUPPLY VEHICLES WERE ON A RIDGE BEHIND –
THE MAJOR IS SIGNALLING FOR US TO PULL BACK! HE KNOWS WE ARE IN RANGE OF THE GUNS!
AIEEE!
UP ON THE WALLS – THE ENEMY HAS LONG-RANGE ANTI-TANK GUNS!

BUT THEY HAD BEEN SPOTTED –
THAT TANKER SURE IS A BEAUT TARGET! WATCH ME TURN IT OVER BOYS!
AND –
AAAH! WE'RE HIT!
JUMP! IT'S GOING OVER THE EDGE!
THE HEAVY TANKER CAREERED DOWN THE SLOPE –
THOSE MAD ANZACS ARE PLAYING WITH US!
SIR! WE CAN'T TAKE THAT TOWN IN A FRONTAL ASSAULT – AND WE CAN'T LEAVE THE TANKE THERE! IT'LL BE LIKE GIVING THOSE ANZACS A GIFT!
A GIFT THAT IT!
PANZER GRENADIERS–DITCH HELMETS AND RALLY TO ME IN THIS SMOKE! MAYBE WE CAN TRY ONE OF THE OLDEST ARMY TRICKS IN THE WORLD!
THE WATCHING ANZACS CHEERED THROUGH THE LIFTING SHELLSMOKE –
YAHOOOOO – WE HAMMERED THAT MOB SURE ENOUGH!
AN' THEY LEFT THEIR JUICE WAGON UP FOR GRABS– GO GET IT.
KRAUTIE'S RUN FOR IT – THAT HAMME MOB AIN'T GONNA MIX WITH US AGAIN UP ON TO THAT TANKER AND SE WHAT FUEL WE'VE WON!

BEAUT! MUST BE A COUPLA HUNDRED GALLONS AT LEAST!
FIX UP A TOWROPE AND WE'LL CART IT BACK INTO TOWN!

SOON –
WHAT A SCORE WE NOTCHED UP! BREAK OUT THE BEERCRATES AN' WE'LL CELEBRATE TONIGHT!

ATER AS A FEW UARDS KEPT WATCH –
NOT A FLAMIN' PEEP OUT THERE! KRAUTIE WON'T MAKE A MOVE TONIGHT!

BUT, INSIDE THE TANKER –
ALL'S QUIET – BREAK SURFACE, PANZER GRENADIERS!

TWO HOURS IN THIS STINKING MUCK BREATHING THROUGH SAWNOFF GASMASKS WE MUST BE MAD!
QUIET – UNWRAP YOUR GUNS I'M OPENING THE HATCH!

HELLMAN CRAWLED OUT ALONG THE TANKER –
HERE'S TO AUSSIE – HEY. WHAT'S THAT STINK?

ME, ANZAC – I CAME FREE WITH THE PETROL! NOW NOT A MOVE!
S'TRUTH!

HELLMAN'S PANZER GRENADIERS QUICKLY OVERPOWERED THE OTHER GUARDS –
THE GATES – THEY'RE OPENING THE GATES!
JA, ANZACS – THE OLDEST INSIDE JOB OF ALL!
YOU CAME IN INSIDE THAT TANKER A FLAMIN' INSIDE JOB!

THE TROJAN HORSE TRICK WAS FIRST USED HERE IN GREECE. AND WHILE YOUR FRIENDS SLEEP MY FORCE WILL TAKE OVER THE TOWN –
WE'RE NOT ALL ASLEEP, SMART ALEC...
IT'S JIMBO...
HELLMAN GRABBED THE CRICKET BAT...
FLAMIN' KRAUTIES EVERYWHERE!
TEUFEL – ANOTHER MAD ANZAC AND HE'S GOING TO FLING A GRENADE AT THE TANKER!
SEE YOU IN HELL, KRAUTIES!
HELLMAN SWUNG –
THE ANZACS RELUCTANTLY SURRENDERED –
AND, BEFORE OTHER ANZACS, ALERTED BY THE EXPLOSION, COULD SWING INTO ACTION...
WUNDERBAR! HAMMER FORCE IS HERE... WE HAVE WON THE TOWN!
SO, WE HAVE REACHED THE SEA AT LAST! BUT THERE IS STILL ENEMY-HELD COASTLINE TO THE SOUTH TO GAIN BEFORE WE'VE WON ALL GREECE. HERE'S YOUR SNORKEL BACK, WAGNER – BUT WE CAN'T BREATHE EASY YET!

HAMMER FORCE RACES TO SECURE A VITAL BRIDGE NEXT WEEK !

MAJOR KURT HELLMAN. . .KING OF THE PANZERS!

GREECE, LATE APRIL, 1941. THE GERMANS HAVE OVERRUN MOST OF THE MAINLAND AND NOW PUSH FOR THE SOUTHERN PART KNOWN AS THE PELOPONNESOS. AMONG THE PANZER UNITS HEADING THAT WAY IS MAJOR KURT HELLMAN'S 'HAMMER FORCE'— AND HELLMAN HAS RACED ON AHEAD OF HIS OTHER TANKS. . .

PARACHUTES IN THE SKY TO THE SOUTH, SIR! OUR AIRBORNE FORCES MUST BE ATTACKING THE CORINTH CANAL!

KEEP AT HIGH SPEED! THOSE PARATROOPERS MAY NEED A PANZER TO HELP THEM!

GHOST MOUNTAINS

GREECE

THERMOPYLAI

CORINTH CANAL

PELOPONNESOS

CRETE

HELLMAN OF HAMMER FORCE

HELLMAN CHECKED HIS MAP—
BUT IN THESE HIGH, WINDING MOUNTAIN ROADS IT'LL TAKE US HOURS TO REACH THEM! THOSE PARAS ARE ON THEIR OWN RIGHT NOW!

DUG IN AROUND THE DROP ZONES WERE TOUGH ALLIED UNITS—
AIEEEE!
ALL SPREAD OUT LIKE A LINE O'DIRTY WASHING! PUT 'EM THROUGH THE WRINGER, BOYS!

THE GERMAN AIRBORNE TROOPERS WERE BADLY MAULED. . .
GET TO OUR WEAPON CONTAINERS — GET THEM OR WE'LL NEVER TAKE THE BRIDGE!

HIGH ABOVE –
MEIN GOTT – THOSE PARAS ARE BEING CUT TO BITS!
SO ARE THEIR PLANES! LOOK AT THAT BLAZING JUNKERS!
OUT OF THE TANK, FAST – AND TRY TO HELP!
BUT –
ALL THE CREW ARE DEAD, SIR AND THOSE PARAS THEY DROPPED WILL BE DEAD MEN, TOO! IT'LL TAKE US HOURS BY ROAD TO GET TO THE CANAL!
HELLMAN PICKED UP SALVAGED EQUIPMENT FROM THE AIRCRAFT WRECK –
UNLESS WE DO SOME DROPPING OURSELVES! WE FORGET ABOUT THE ROAD AND TAKE THE PANZER STRAIGHT DOWN THE SLOPE!
RACE DOWN THE SIDE OF THIS LIKE A CRESTA RUN? IN A TANK?
IT'S SUICIDE!
BUT I WILL NOT ORDER YOU TO DO IT! YOU MUST MAKE UP YOUR OWN MINDS...
WE COME, TOO! THIS PANZER'S OURS AS MUCH AS YOURS – SO WE'LL ALL BREAK OUR BONES TOGETHER!
OKAY, KESSEL – IT'S YOUR CRESTA RUN!
HOLD TIGHT, CREW!

AND HERE WE GO!
22 TONS OF PANZER STEEL HURLED DOWN THE SLOPE –
GOOD STEERING, KESSEL– KEEP HER WEAVING!
BUT –
NO GOOD, SIR, WE'RE SLIDING. THE SLOPE'S TOO STEEP AND OUR TRACKS AREN'T BITING!
THIS IS IT... WE CAN'T SLOW DOWN! THE WHOLE TANK WILL SOMERSAULT!
ONE CHANCE! THESE PARACHUTE PACKS WE TOOK FROM THE PLANE! RAM 'EM INTO THE REAR HATCHES...FAST!
THIS HAD BETTER WORK OR WE'RE ALL DEAD!
THE GIANT PARACHUTES, DESIGNED TO HOLD HEAVY WEIGHTS, SNAPPED OPEN –
IT'S WORKING, SIR – THEY'RE SLOWING US DOWN! I'VE GOT CONTROL AGAIN!

ITS WEIGHT HELD IN CHECK, THE PANZER SWERVED DOWN THE SLOPES –
YOU DID IT, KESSEL! YOU DID YOUR MOUNTAIN RUN!
THANKS TO THE MAJOR!
STOP THE BACKSLAPPING – WE'RE ALMOST AT THE BRIDGE! BATTLE STATIONS, CREW!

DONNER! A PANZER AND IT DROVE HERE DOWN THE SIDE OF THAT MOUNTAIN!
OKAY, YOU JUMPERS – YOU'VE GOT SOME ARMOUR AT LAST! ATTACK!

FULL SPEED AHEAD – HIT THEM FIRST!

DEPRESS THE GUN! GET THAT TANK!

BUT –

NOW IT'S YOUR TURN TO JUMP!

HE'S BULLDOZED OUR GUN OFF THE BRIDGE!

SOON THE BRIDGE WAS IN GERMAN HANDS AND SUPPORT FORCES WERE COMING UP FAST–

NOW WE CAN FAN OUT ALL OVER THE PELOPONNESOS... AND SOON GREECE AND THE EUROPEAN MAINLAND WILL BE OURS!

THANKS TO MEN LIKE YOU, MAJOR! BUT WHERE DO YOU GO NEXT TO BATTLE?

EAST... THAT'S WHERE I BET BERLIN IS LOOKING. WE'LL BE REFITTED AND REINFORCED FAST, I KNOW THAT... BUT WILL LUCK KEEP RIDING WITH US WHEN 'HAMMER FORCE' HITS RUSSIA?

JOIN HELLMAN FOR THE INVASION OF RUSSIA IN TWO WEEKS' TIME !

BLAST INTO ACTION AND "OPERATION BARBAROSSA" WITH HELLMAN!

JUNE, 1941 . . . AND AFTER TWO YEARS OF VICTORY IN THE WEST THE GERMAN PANZERS NOW TURN EAST . . . TO TAKE ON MIGHTY RUSSIA. ASSEMBLED UNDER CAMOUFLAGE ON THE POLISH FRONTIER ARE DOZENS OF PANZER DIVISIONS, AMONG THEM MAJOR KURT HELLMAN'S 'HAMMER FORCE'.

COFFEE FOR YOU AND YOUR CREW, MAJOR!

THANKS, MULLER. NOW BE PREPARED—THE BIG MOMENT IS ALMOST HERE!

HELLMAN ON THE RUSSIAN FRONT

INSIDE HELLMAN'S PANZER IV—
I CUT THE KING—A GOOD OMEN, KESSEL!
JA, RUSSIA'S THE KING SIZE TARGET. OUR BATTLES AGAINST THE FROGS, TOMMIES AND GREEKS WERE JUST A WARM-UP FOR THIS!
MY CREW IS CONFIDENT, BUT WILL RUSSIA BE AS EASY AS THE OTHER CAMPAIGNS?
HELLMAN'S THOUGHTS FLASHED BACK TO TWO YEARS BEFORE WHEN RUSSIA AND GERMANY HAD BEEN ALLIES AND MILITARY PARTNERS.
A PARTY OF RUSSIAN EXPERTS HAVE COME TO OUR TANK FACTORIES TO SEE OUR PANZERS IN PRODUCTION.

GOTT! THAT PANZER IS SLIPPING FROM THE CONVEYOR BELT! IT WILL TOPPLE ON TO THAT RUSSIAN!
HELLMAN LEAPT FOR A DANGLING FACTORY CHAIN, AND–
OUT OF THE WAY, RUSSIAN MAJOR–BEFORE YOU ARE CRUSHED!
AAAAAARGH!
AND–
THANK YOU, GERMAN! YOU SAVED MY LIFE!
IT WAS NOTHING!
LATER–
GOODBYE, KURT HELLMAN! I HOPE WE MEET AGAIN AS FRIENDS!
I TOO, ALEXEI!
HELLMAN'S THOUGHTS FLASHED BACK AGAIN TO THE PRESENT–
AND NOW I MUST FIGHT AGAINST MEN LIKE ALEXEI!
SIR–LOOK! GUNFLASHES EVERYWHERE! THE INVASION'S STARTING!
THAT MORNING, BEFORE DAWN ON JUNE 22nd, 1941, OPERATION BARBAROSSA WAS UNLEASHED–
FIRE! FIRE! FIRE!
FIRST THE BIG GUNS–THEN THE STUKAS–THEN THE PANZERS GO IN!
HELLMAN'S CREWMEN LEAPT INTO ACTION–
WAGNER AND WEISS! STRIP AWAY THE CAMOUFLAGE! SCHRODER–OPEN RADIO CONTACT! KESSEL–START ENGINES!
PANZERS ROLL!
IN WEDGE FORMATION THE OTHER HAMMER FORCE PANZERS STRUNG OUT BEHIND HELLMAN–
LEUTNANT WITTER–SERGEANT RAUCH – CLOSE YOUR PANZERS UP! ALL SEAL TURRETS TO CROSS THE RIVER BUG AHEAD!

HELLMAN'S PANZERS WERE SPECIALLY WATERPROOFED TO CROSS WIDE RIVERS!
COME ON IN, PANZERMEN— THE WATER'S LOVELY!
BUT, ON THE FAR SIDE OF THE RIVER BUG, RED SOLDIERS WERE REACTING—
KRASNI! KRASNI! THE GERMAN WARDOGS COME! MAN YOUR POSITIONS, COMRADES!
THE SCUM SWIM OVER— OPEN FIRE ON THOSE BOAT-TROOPS FIRST!
ACH-AIEEEEEEEEE!
OUR INFANTRY STORMBOATS ARE BEING CUT TO BITS BY RUSSIANS ON THE FAR BANK!
HELLMAN UNSEALED HIS TURRET HATCH—
ALL OUR BOATS MASSACRED. THE REDS ARE IN HIDDEN POSITIONS — AND SOMEONE'S GOT TO GO OUT AND PINPOINT THEM!
DONNER! THE MAJOR'S LEAPT FOR THAT STORMBOAT!
AND, AS HELLMAN STEERED FOR THE BANK—
I SEE THEM. . . TANKS AND INFANTRY HIDDEN IN THOSE TREES . . . WAITING FOR MY TANKS TO GET IN RANGE!
BUT IF I STEER THE STORMBOAT RIGHT AT THE TARGET, MY PANZERS WILL KNOW WHERE THE RED TANKS ARE!
THE MAJOR'S AIMED THE BOAT AT THAT CLUMP OF TREES - THAT'S WHERE THE HEAVY STUFF MUST BE!

HELLMAN WAS RIGHT!
OPEN FIRE . . . ALL GUNS RANGE ON THOSE TREES!
AIEEEEEEEEEE!
GREAT—MY TANK GUNS HAVE CAUGHT THE WHOLE RED TANK NEST!
HELLMAN EMERGED ON TO THE BANK—
THE WHOLE RED POSITION SILENT AND SMOKING. BUT ONE MAN STILL ALIVE . . . A RED ARMY OFFICER!
GERMAN WARDOG! DIE!
HELLMAN RECOGNISED THE BLACKENED SLAV FACE—
GOTT IN—ALEXEI! MAJOR ALEXEI—IT'S ME, KURT HELLMAN!
I SEE YOU, WAR-DOG, DIE!
HELLMAN FIRED FIRST—BLOWING HIS GUN AWAY—
NOW GIVE UP, ALEXEI—THERE IS NO NEED TO GO ON FIGHTING!
NIET!
I SAID GIVE UP—YOU'VE LOST! ALEXEI, DON'T MAKE ME DO IT!
AIEEEEEEEE-URRAAAIIIII!
NEXT SECOND—
AIEEEEEEEE!
GOT HIM, SIR! HE WAS ALMOST ON YOU!
MY HAMMER FORCE PANZERS ARE HERE—THEY SHOT BEFORE I COULD!
WHY, ALEXEI—WHY DID YOU GO ON FIGHTING?
YOU DO NOT UNDERSTAND THE RUSSIAN MAN, HELLMAN . . .
BY SETTING FOOT IN RUSSIA YOU HAVE SET ONE FOOT IN HELL. . . YOU HAVE WOKEN THE RUSSIAN BEAR. NOW YOU WILL FIGHT A WAR YOU HAVE SEEN NOTHING LIKE BEFORE . . . WAIT TILL YOU SEE THE SURPRISES WE HAVE IN STORE!
RUSSKY'S DEAD, SIR—TALKED LIKE A RED FANATIC!
YET HE WAS NO RED FANATIC BEFORE!
SERGEANT KESSEL MUTTERED—
ONE OF MY CARDS WEDGED IN THE HATCH, SIR—ACE OF SPADES! GOTT, THAT'S A BAD OMEN FOR THE 'OSTKREIG'
THE 'OSTKREIG' . . . THE RUSSIAN FRONT! WHAT IF ALEXEI IS RIGHT. IS RUSSIA THE PLACE WHERE THE PANZERS ROLL TO THEIR HELL?
MORE THRILLING ACTION WITH HELLMAN NEXT WEEK !

KING OF THE PANZERS – THAT'S KURT HELLMAN !

SUMMER, 1941 – THE GERMAN PANZER GROUPS GRIND OVER THE RUSSIAN PLAINS AND, AS THEY GO FORWARD, THE FUHRER'S RECORDED VOICE SOUNDS IN EVERY TANK RADIO, INCLUDING THOSE OF PANZER UNIT, 'HAMMER FORCE', LED BY MAJOR KURT HELLMAN –
MAJOR KURT HELLMAN
UNTEROFFIZIER MASCHLER
LEUTNANT WITTER
REMEMBER—WE HAVE ONLY TO KICK IN THE RUSSIAN DOOR AND THE WHOLE ROTTING STRUCTURE COMES CRASHING DOWN !
HELLMAN
ON THE RUSSIAN FRONT
INSIDE HELLMAN'S TANK –
THE FUHRER'S WORDS MAKE IT SOUND EASY, MAJOR!
THERE'S SOMEONE WHO'S BELIEVED HIS EVERY WORD – MASCHLER!
UNTEROFFIZIER MASCHLER WAS AN ARDENT NAZI –
WHAT A SPEECH FROM THE FUHRER! JA, RUSSIA'S LIKE A ROTTING DOOR ALL RIGHT – JUST LIKE THAT DOOR THERE!
SEE . . . THE DOOR COMES DOWN WITH ONE KICK OF A PANZER BOOT!

ACH – RUSSIAN RABBLE INSIDE! I'LL SHUT THEM UP WITH A STICK-GRENADE!
NIET! NIET!

NO, MASCHLER! MY UNIT DOES NOT BUTCHER WOMEN AND CHILDREN!

CURSE YOU, HELLMAN – BUT I'LL TAKE THIS DOOR AS A PRIZE!

THE NAZI'S TAKEN HIS DOOR AND LOOK AT THE WORDS HE'S PAINTED ON – THE 'RED DOOR'!
DIE ROTEN TÜR
HE'S WRONG IF HE THINKS THEY'LL ALL COME CRASHING DOWN LIKE THAT ONE. MOVE OUT – PANZERS ROLL!

HELLMAN'S THREE TANKS DROVE INTO DARKNESS –
SLOW DOWN . . . SWAMPLAND AHEAD! WE'LL GO THROUGH IN SINGLE FILE! MASCHLER DROP BACK AND LET WITTER OVERTAKE!

GO TO HELL, HERR MAJOR! I'LL KEEP THE LEAD OVER BOY-SCOUT WITTER!
DRIVER, CUT IN!
LOOK OUT, MASCHLER! YOU'VE DRIVEN US INTO THE SWAMP!
TOUGH LUCK, WITTER – YOU SHOULD HANDLE YOUR PANZER BETTER!

THE LITTLE NAZI MEANT THAT, MAJOR!
I KNOW, KESSEL! HEY, MASCHLER . . . STOP YOUR TANK IMMEDIATELY!

I CAN'T HELP WITTER! HE'S STUCK THERE UNTIL THE SUPPORT WAVE COMES WITH TOW CRANES!
HE NEEDS A RAMP OF SOLID WOOD TO HELP HIM OUT . . .

. . . AND YOUR PRIZED DOOR WILL DO THE TRICK! TAKE IT FROM HIM, KESSEL!
YOU BET, SIR!

THE DOOR WAS PLACED BENEATH THE TRACKS . . .
SCOUT AHEAD, MASCHLER, WHILE WE GET WITTER OUT. BUT DON'T GO NEAR ANYTHING SUSPICIOUS!

...OON –
SHE'S COMING – BUT THE DOOR IS SPLINTERING!
IT'LL GET YOU OUT BEFORE IT BREAKS UP!

MASCHLER'S TANK DROVE ON –
THAT HELLMAN IS A TRAITOR TO THE NAZI CAUSE! I'LL TRIP HIM UP SOON AND THEN I'LL HAVE HIS MAJOR'S BARS!
BIG HOUSE AHEAD, SIR!

ALL DESERTED AND LOOK AT THE SIZE OF ITS FRONT DOOR – WHAT A TROPHY THAT'LL MAKE! FORWARD ENGINES. . .
THE MAJOR SAID NOT TO APPROACH ANYTHING SUSPICIOUS!
ACH, THERE'S NO RUSSKIES AROUND AND I WANT THAT DOOR!

HA – IT'S LOCKED – BUT I'LL HAVE IT OFF IN NO TIME!

IT'S FREE! WHAT A BEAUTY TO CARRY WITH US –
GOTT IN – SOMETHING INSIDE THE HOUSE!

RUSSIAN TANK! BUT I'VE NEVER SEEN ONE LIKE IT BEFORE. . .

NEIN! GET BACK!

AIEEEEEEEEE!
MASCHLER'S CREW ACTED FAST, BUT–
OUR SHELL HASN'T STOPPED IT!
AND THE UNTEROFFIZIER CRUSHED!
NEARBY, IN THE SWAMPS –
TANK FIRING AHEAD . . . MASCHLER'S TANK MUST BE IN TROUBLE! LET'S GET THERE!
TOO LATE! THE PANZER ABLAZE AND THE CREW BLOWN APART!
AND MASCHLER CRUSHED TO A PULP! WHAT KIND OF MONSTER TANK DID THIS?
LOOK AT THE SIZE OF ITS TRACKING!
SO THE REDS MUST HAVE A NEW MYSTERY TANK – AND THIS ONE WAS WAITING IN AMBUSH BEHIND THAT DOOR! THE FUHRER IS WRONG – THERE ARE MANY MORE DIRTY SURPRISES OPENING UP FOR US ON THIS CURSED RUSSIAN FRONT!

JOIN HELLMAN FOR MORE TOUGH TANK ACTION NEXT WEEK !

TWO MEN PIT THEMSELVES AGAINST A BRAND NEW T-34 !

MASCHLER
USSIA, SUMMER, 1941. THE INVADING GERMAN PANZERS ROLL N EAST ACROSS THE VAST STEPPES BUT THEY ARE MEETING URPRISES AND SETBACKS FOR THE FIRST TIME. PANZER MAJOR URT HELLMAN'S UNIT OF THREE PANZERS OPERATING IN WAMP COUNTRY, HAS JUST LOST ONE OF ITS TANKS TO A YSTERY ARMOURED ATTACKER.
MASCHLER AND HIS CREW CUT TO BITS BY A NEW RED TERROR TANK. NOW IT'S HIDING IN THESE SWAMPS AND SOMEHOW YOU MUST BEAT IT, HELLMAN.

HELLMAN ON THE RUSSIAN FRONT

HEY, GERMAN! NONE OF YOU WILL LEAVE THESE SWAMPS ALIVE!
IVAN VOICES!

COME ON, YOU DIRTY RUSSKIES – SHOW YOURSELVES!
WITTER! SAVE THAT SPANDAU AMMO!

I–I'M SORRY, MAJOR.
IT'S RUSSIA, SIR. IT'S BEGINNING TO GET TO EVERYONE!
THAT'S ENOUGH! INTO THE TANKS, NOW!

WHATEVER THIS RED TANK IS, WE'RE NOT GOING TO BE SITTING TARGETS FOR IT. START ENGINES AND LET'S TRY AND GET CLEAR OF THE SWAMPS!

THE GERMANS ARE MOVING! SIGNAL THE T34 TO GET READY!
DA!

ONLY ONE TRACK AND NARROW AS A TIGHTROPE. KEEP RIGHT BEHIND ME, WITTER!
J-JAWOHL, HERR MAJOR.

BUT, AS WITTER'S PANZER PASSED —
SPRING THE TRAP!
ACHTUNG! BEHIND US!
IT'S THE TERROR TANK! GUNNER SWING AND GET IT! SCHNELL!

BUT THE DEADLY T34 HAD SLOPING TOUGH ARMOUR WHICH COULD SHRUG OFF ANY GERMAN TANK SHELL!
NO USE, FRITZ— NOW TASTE THIS!
YAHHHHHH! BALE OUT!

BUT —
GOTT! WE'RE NECK-DEEP IN MUD!
SHOVE THE FRITZIES INTO THE SLIME WHERE THEY BELONG!
AIEEEEEEEEEE!

HELLMAN'S PANZER WAS REVERSING BACK AS QUICKLY AS IT COULD TO HELP.
COME IN, PANZER TWO! COME IN!
TOO LATE! YOU HEAR THAT SUCKING SOUND? YOU ARE TALKING TO MUD, GERMAN!

YOU CAN RUN LIKE A SCARED SWAMP FOX, BUT WE'LL RUN YOU DOWN, TOO!
THE IVANS ARE ON OUR RADIO WAVELENGTH!
AND THEY'LL EASILY CATCH UP AND KILL US! WHAT DO WE DO?

HELLMAN WROTE A QUICK NOTE –
PANIC
THE MAJOR WANTS ME TO ACT PANICKY. HE MUST HAVE A PLAN.

KESSEL SWUNG THE CONTROLS.
NEIN, NEIN! MUST GET OUT OF HERE! THOSE RED DEVILS MUST NOT CATCH US!

BEHIND THE T34 WAS CATCHING UP.
HA! LOOK AT THEM STUMBLING INTO TREES! AND HEAR THEM SCREAMING IN BLIND PANIC ON THEIR RADIO!

A BEND IN THE TRACK HIDES US FOR A MOMENT! NOW'S OUR CHANCE
TAKE OUT THE HEAVY SPANNERS AND DON GOGGLES, WAGNER – WE'RE BALING OUT!

DRIVE ON, KESSEL!
JAWOHL, HERR MAJOR!

MOMENTS LATER THE T34 AND ITS INFANTRY FLASHED PAST -
WE'LL SOON HAVE OUR THIRD KILL!
THEN THEY'LL BE LYING IN THE MUD LIKE THOSE LOGS!

STAVA! HIDING IN THE MUD!
WE ALREADY ARE! HIT THEM, WAGNER!

WAGNER – WATCH OUT! TANK HATCH CLOSING!
NIET–YAIEEEEEE!
A SPANNER WILL STOP THAT!
DIE, REDS!
AIEE!
HIT THEIR AMMO – JUMP FOR IT!
HELLMAN'S PANZER IV CAME UP –
YOU DID IT, MAJOR! MADE THEM THINK WE WERE SCARED AND THEN HIT THEM UNEXPECTEDLY!
JA, THREE TANKS AND THEIR CREWS SLAUGHTERED IN THESE SWAMPS AND NO PRISONERS TAKEN. NOW I KNOW THE SCORE . . . IT'S GOING TO GET RAWER AND DIRTIER ON THE RUSSIAN FRONT!

NEXT WEEK – WINTER ARRIVES, AND WITH IT RUSSIA'S COUNTER-ATTACK !

HELLMAN'S HAMMER FORCE – FIGHTING FOR SURVIVAL IN RUSSIA !

ECEMBER, 1941–THE GERMAN ADVANCE GRINDS TO A HALT
EFORE THE GATES OF MOSCOW, FROZEN BY THE TERRIBLE
USSIAN WINTER. NOW AT LAST THE RUSSIANS UNLEASH
HEIR COUNTER-ATTACK OF MEN AND MACHINES MADE FOR
NOWFIGHTING . . . TOUGH SIBERIAN SOLDIERS AND WAVES
F DEADLY T34 TANKS!

URRAYA MOSCAWA! WITH THE SNOW COMES THE GERMANS' SLAUGHTER!

DUG IN BEFORE MOSCOW WAS MAJOR KURT HELLMAN'S PANZER REGIMENT, DECIMATED BY ITS LOSSES IN THE RUSSIAN CAMPAIGN.

THE SIBERIANS! THE SIBERIANS ARE COMING WITH THE T34s !

THEY'RE STRIKING NOW WHEN WE'RE HALF-DEAD! MAN THE PANZER, CREW!

HELLMAN ON THE RUSSIAN FRONT

UT–
THE ENGINE'S FROZEN STIFF, SIR–WE CAN'T START HER !
THAT CAMPFIRE, IT'S OUR ONE CHANCE!

MOMENTS LATER–
THE ENGINE'S STARTED, MAJOR–YOU DID IT? BUT WHERE DO WE ROLL TO? THOSE T34s'LL TEAR OUR LONE PANZER APART!
MAKE FOR THAT SNOWDRIFT!

THAT'S IT–THROW THOSE REDHOT ASHES OVER THE ENGINE HATCH! WE'VE GOT TO WARM IT UP!
AND FAST! I CAN HEAR THE RED TANKS APPROACHING!
NEARBY, PANZER INFANTRY WAS DIGGING IN FEVERISHLY–
WHERE'S HELLMAN AND HIS TANK GONE?
THEY'VE RUN–LEFT US DOG SOLDIERS IN THE LURCH, DAMN THEM!

THE T34s RACED IN–
HA–ONLY GERMAN INFANTRY HERE! OUR SIBERIANS WILL ENJOY THEMSELVES!
BUT–
PREPARE TO HIT THE SECOND TANK IN ITS WEAK SPOT . . . THE ENGINE!
NOW, KESSEL! FORWARD AND FIRE!
GOTT–HELLMAN'S PANZER WAS HIDING IN THAT SNOWDRIFT!
AND–
AIEEEE!
STAVA–THE PANZER'S BURNT OUR COMRADE! TURN AND TAKE IT!
RACE IN BEHIND THE BURNING T34, KESSEL!
NOW YOU DIE– GERMAN–FIRE!
CURSE HIM–HE MANOEUVRED BEHIND OUR BROTHER'S BURNING TANK JUST IN TIME!
KEEP GOING, KESSEL– RAM IT! RAM IT!
STAVA! HE'S GOING TO BULLDOZE IT ON TO US!
THE FIRST T34 SMASHED INTO THE SECOND, SPRAYING IT WITH BLAZING FUEL!
WE'VE TAMED THE T34s– NOW ITS UP TO OUR INFANTRY TO DEAL WITH THE SIBERIANS!
THE SIBERIAN SNOW-SOLDIERS, SUDDENLY CAUGHT WITHOUT TANK SUPPORT, WERE CUT DOWN BY THE FIERCE GERMAN FIRE . . .
AIEEEEEE!
BACK! BACK TO THE CITY,

AS HELLMAN'S CREW BALED OUT OF THEIR BADLY DAMAGED TANK . . .
WE DID IT, SIR–HELD THAT ATTACK!
BUT NOW WHAT? ALL WE CAN DO IS FREEZE TO DEATH IN PEACE!
OUR INFANTRY IS FIGHTING OVER THAT RUSSIAN WINTER EQUIPMENT!
JA . . . AND I DO NOT LIKE IT! CUT THAT OUT, PANZER GRENADIERS, AND BUNDLE THOSE SUITS TOGETHER!
WHY STOP US, HELLMAN? AT LEAST WE WON'T FREEZE IN THESE SUITS . . .
BUT–
WHAT THE–? HE'S TOSSING THE SNOW-SUITS ON TO THE FIRE!
JA! I'M NOT LETTING YOU FIGHT OVER THEM LIKE A PACK OF WILD DOGS! REMEMBER THAT YOU ARE WEHRMACHT SOLDIERS!
DON'T GIVE US THAT, HELLMAN–WE ALL KNOW BERLIN DOESN'T GIVE A DAMN ABOUT US!
THE MAJOR LOOKS TO HAVE A MUTINY ON HIS HANDS, BUT NOBODY TOUCHES HIM WHILE I'M ON MY FEET!
HOLD IT, WAGNER–HE'S GOING OVER TO THAT ABANDONED ARMY TRUCK!
WELL, WELL–DRUMS OF WHITE PAINT. OPEN THEM UP!
THE TANK MAJOR HAS GONE SNOW-CRAZY! LET'S . . .
LET'S DO NOTHING YET, SOLDIER.
NOW WATCH ME AND EVERY MAN COPY! COVER YOURSELF FROM HEAD TO FOOT IN WHITE PAINT! HELMET, FACE, BOOTS, GUN, EVERYTHING!
BUT . . .
JUST DO AS THE MAJOR SAYS, MAN.
RELUCTANTLY, THE WEARY MEN OBEYED. SOON EVERY MAN WAS COVERED–
IN THIS SNOW THE PAINT MAKES EXCELLENT CAMOUFLAGE. NOW, GET READY TO MOVE OUT! WE WERE ORDERED NOT TO MOVE BACK . . . BUT NOBODY SAID ANYTHING ABOUT GOING FORWARD!
FORWARD?
HELLMAN LOOKED EAST–
JA–I'D RATHER DIE A FIGHTER THAN A FROZEN HUNK OF MEAT! IF BERLIN WON'T GIVE US WINTER EQUIPMENT WE'LL GET IT FROM MOSCOW. LET'S GO!
JUST A FEW DOZEN MEN MARCHING UP TO IVAN'S DOOR. IT'S CRAZY BUT THE MAJOR KNOWS IT'S OUR ONLY CHANCE. BEWARE, MOSCOW, HERE COMES THE MAD MAJOR AND HIS GHOSTS!
WILL HELLMAN'S DEADLY GAMBLE COME OFF? SEE NEXT WEEK!

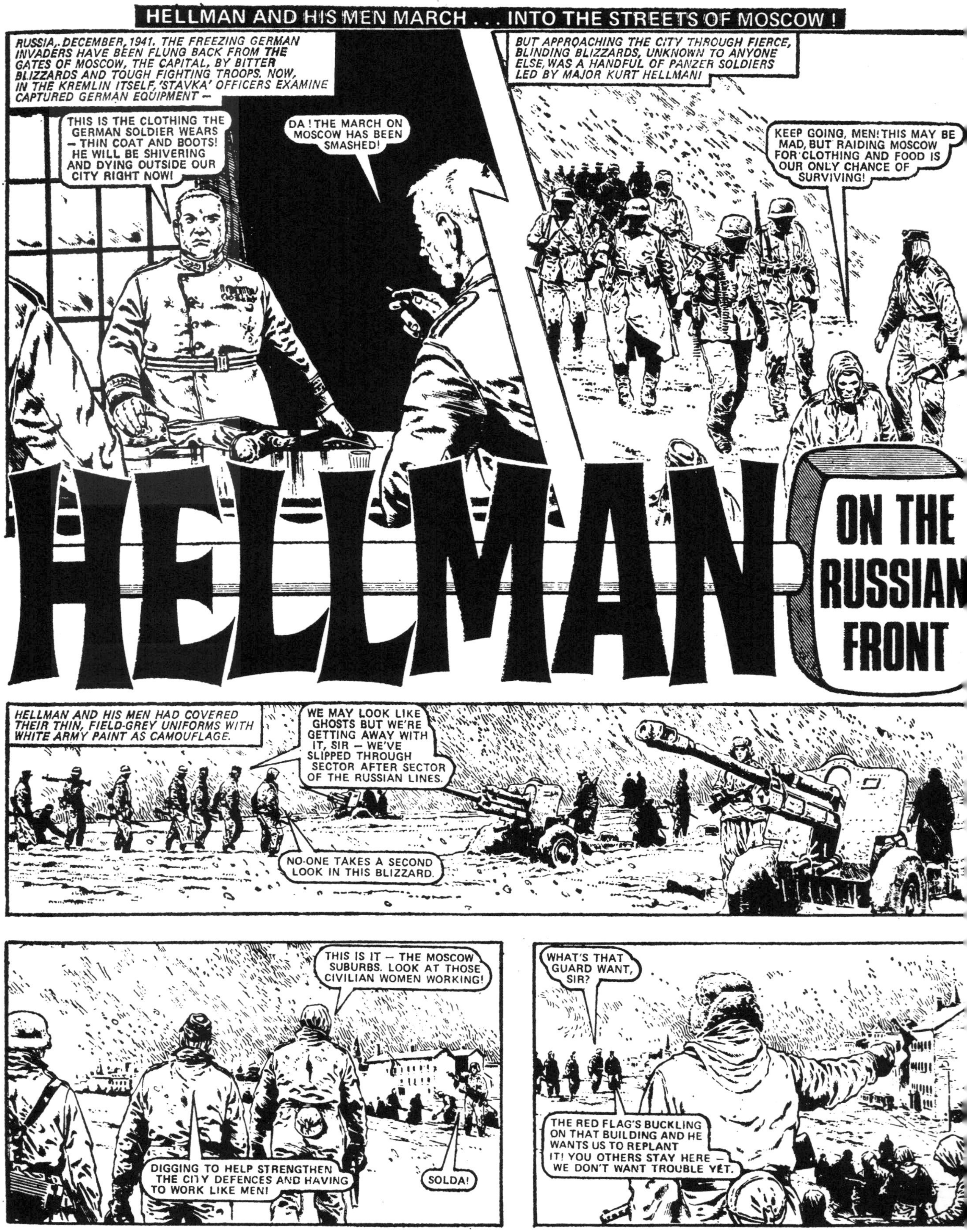

HELLMAN AND HIS MEN MARCH . . . INTO THE STREETS OF MOSCOW !

RUSSIA, DECEMBER, 1941. THE FREEZING GERMAN INVADERS HAVE BEEN FLUNG BACK FROM THE GATES OF MOSCOW, THE CAPITAL, BY BITTER BLIZZARDS AND TOUGH FIGHTING TROOPS. NOW, IN THE KREMLIN ITSELF, 'STAVKA' OFFICERS EXAMINE CAPTURED GERMAN EQUIPMENT –

THIS IS THE CLOTHING THE GERMAN SOLDIER WEARS – THIN COAT AND BOOTS! HE WILL BE SHIVERING AND DYING OUTSIDE OUR CITY RIGHT NOW!

DA! THE MARCH ON MOSCOW HAS BEEN SMASHED!

BUT APPROACHING THE CITY THROUGH FIERCE, BLINDING BLIZZARDS, UNKNOWN TO ANYONE ELSE, WAS A HANDFUL OF PANZER SOLDIERS LED BY MAJOR KURT HELLMAN!

KEEP GOING, MEN! THIS MAY BE MAD, BUT RAIDING MOSCOW FOR CLOTHING AND FOOD IS OUR ONLY CHANCE OF SURVIVING!

HELLMAN ON THE RUSSIAN FRONT

HELLMAN AND HIS MEN HAD COVERED THEIR THIN, FIELD-GREY UNIFORMS WITH WHITE ARMY PAINT AS CAMOUFLAGE.
WE MAY LOOK LIKE GHOSTS BUT WE'RE GETTING AWAY WITH IT, SIR – WE'VE SLIPPED THROUGH SECTOR AFTER SECTOR OF THE RUSSIAN LINES.
NO-ONE TAKES A SECOND LOOK IN THIS BLIZZARD.

THIS IS IT – THE MOSCOW SUBURBS. LOOK AT THOSE CIVILIAN WOMEN WORKING!
DIGGING TO HELP STRENGTHEN THE CITY DEFENCES AND HAVING TO WORK LIKE MEN!
SOLDA!

WHAT'S THAT GUARD WANT, SIR?
THE RED FLAG'S BUCKLING ON THAT BUILDING AND HE WANTS US TO REPLANT IT! YOU OTHERS STAY HERE – WE DON'T WANT TROUBLE YET.

HELLMAN CLIMBED UP WITH SERGEANT KESSEL AND GUNNER WAGNER.
WHO'D HAVE THOUGHT WE'D FIND OURSELVES SECURIN' A RED FLAG?
IT GIVES US A GOOD VIEW OF THE MOSCOW STREETS AND OVER THERE'S WHAT WE WANT. . .A RED ARMY SUPPLY DEPOT!
AFTER SECURING THE FLAG–
TANKSELO! TANKSELO-DA, DA!
THAT T34–IT'S ASKING FOR DIRECTIONS TO THE DEPOT! FOLLOW IT!
ACH, ONCE AGAIN WE TRUDGE BEHIND VERDAMMT TANKS!
SHUT IT, SPANDAU, AND KEEP YOUR GUN HANDY, WE MAY NEED IT.
SO FAR SO GOOD.
THE MEN WERE COMPLAINING OF THE COLD BUT THIS IS MAKING THEM SWEAT.
TWO STREETS LATER –
STOI KTO! NKVD!
WE'VE REACHED THE DEPOT ALL RIGHT – BUT SEE WHO ITS GUARDS ARE – THE NKVD!
THEY'VE SEEN THROUGH THE DISGUISE!
STAVA
EVERY MAN OPEN FIRE!
AIEEEE!
HELLMAN LEAPT ABOARD THE T34–
SORRY, TANKMEN, WE'VE GOT TO TAKE CARE OF YOU, TOO!
AIEEEE!

AND, AFTER A SHORT BUT BITTER STRUGGLE –
ALL THE GUARDS DEALT WITH, SIR – WE'RE IN THE DEPOT!
GUT – WAGNER SWING THE TANK AROUND AND GUARD THE GATES FOR US! YOU WITH THE SPANDAU HELP HIM!

THE GRUMBLING MACHINE-GUNNER SPAT –
ACH, STILL I FREEZE IN THIS SNOW!
YOU WERE GIVEN AN ORDER, SPANDAU– SET IT UP AND EYES PEELED!

INSIDE –
LOOK AT THESE WINTER SUITS– LINED WITH SIBERIAN FUR!
JA, WE'VE GOT WHAT WE CAME FOR.. EVERY MAN DON ONE AND LET'S GO!

BUT AT THE GATES –
TANKS AND SOLDIERS COMING EVERYWHERE! COME ON, SPANDAU – YOU AN' ME GET OUR SHOTS IN FIRST!
YOU'VE GOT THEIR RANGE, TANK BOY! NOW LET ME SCATTER THE INFANTRY!

BUT NEXT MOMENT –
AUEEEEEE!
YAHHHHH!

WAGNER–HE'S HIT!

I'VE HAD IT, SIR. I'LL STAY WITH THE TANK AN' COVER YOUR ESCAPE. ONE FAVOUR – THAT SPANDAUMAN'S DONE NOTHING BUT GRUMBLE ABOUT THE COLD – HELP HIM COME IN HERE FOR A WARM SEAT AT LAST.

AND –
YOU'RE A TANKMAN NOW, AND YOU CAN DIE ALONGSID ME, DOG SOLDIER.
DANKE.

MAJOR, SIR – THE OTHERS HAVE TAKEN THE SNOW-SUITS AND SPLIT INTO PAIRS TO GET AWAY – NOW US! LET'S GO!
WAGNER, I . . .
GET GOING, SIR – SEE YOU!

AS HELLMAN AND HIS SERGEANT SLIPPED DOWN A SIDESTREET THEY HEARD THE LAST DEFIANT SHOTS.
ЖУНТ
THE RUSSIANS HAVE GONE IN FOR THE KILL. WAGNER AND THAT SPAN-DAUMAN –
THEY'LL DIE WARM, SIR – AND WITH SOME REASON, NOT LIKE DOGS IN THE SNOW. NOW WE MUST THINK FAST IF WE WANT TO GET OUT OF MOSCOW ALIVE.

NEXT MORNING ON THE CITY OUTSKIRTS –
ATTENTION, COMRADES AND CITIZENS – THIS IS THE KREMLIN! A RAID BY GERMAN TERRORISTS WAS WIPED OUT LAST NIGHT. ANY SURVIVORS WILL BE CAUGHT SOON. NOW BACK TO WORK FOR MOSCOW AND THE FRONT!

TWO NKVD GUARDS PASSED A PAIR OF WOMEN –
THAT WAS ALL, WOMAN-WORKER, GET ON WITH THE DIGGING!
DA, PLENTY MORE WORK FOR YOU ON THE RUSSIAN FRONT! HA, HA!

WHEWW – IF THEY'D TAKEN A GOOD LOOK AT US 'WOMEN WORKERS'.
NOT MUCH LONGER NOW, KESSEL – WHEN IT'S DARK WE WORK OUR WAY THROUGH THE LINES BACK TO OUR OWN MEN.
TWELVE HOURS LATER HELLMAN WAS BACK IN GERMAN LINES –
THE MAJOR – HE MADE IT! HALF OF US GOT BACK FROM MOSCOW, SIR!
AND WHAT SOUVENIRS, SIR – NOW IN THESE SUITS WE CAN DO SOME FIGHTING!

JA, I'M BACK AND READY TO FIGHT AGAIN. FIGHTING NOT ONLY FOR MY COUNTRY, BUT FOR WAGNER'S MEMORY AS WELL!

MORE THRILLING ACTION WITH HELLMAN NEXT WEEK !

HELLMAN RETURNS TO GERMANY . . . BUT THE HOMECOMING IS ANYTHING BUT WARM !
HELLMAN
ON THE RUSSIAN FRONT
1945-THE FOURTH YEAR OF THE RUSSIAN FRONT. NOW, AS THE MIGHTY HORDES OF THE RUSSIAN ARMY SWEEP INTO THE FATHERLAND, ONLY DETERMINED VETERANS LIKE MAJOR KURT HELLMAN – RECENTLY ESCAPED ACROSS THE BALTIC – STILL HAVE SOME FIGHT LEFT IN THEM.
BACK ON GERMAN SOIL AT LAST, SIR, AND OUR BACKS ARE REALLY TO THE WALL THIS TIME.
JA, NOW WE'RE SLAP BANG IN FRONT OF BERLIN!
WITH HELLMAN WERE THE TWO TANKMEN WHO'D BEEN WITH HIM SINCE 1943 – BIG MAX AND DEKKER.
WE'VE BEEN UP AGAINST IT BEFORE – REMEMBER?
JA – KURSK, EIGHTEEN MONTHS AGO!
"DEKKER AND I WERE CONVICT SOLDIERS IN OZEL PRISON, WITH SLIMY MP WATCHDOGS ALL ROUND US. THEY WERE SCARED, KNOWING THE RUSSKIES WERE COMIN' THEIR WAY!"
"THEN THE WATCHDOGS CLEARED OUT, LEAVIN' THE GATES UNGUARDED."
THIS IS OUR CHANCE – WE CAN GET FREE BEFORE THE RUSSIANS COME!
STAND BACK – GIVE MAX SOME ROOM!
"BUT, WHEN THE GATES OPENED WE GOT OUR FIRST GLIMPSE OF YOU."
A TIGER TANK BARRING OUR WAY – WITH AN OFFICER ON IT!
AND HE'S ALONE!
NOT FOR LONG – HERE TO TURN Y JAILBIRDS INTO SOLDIERS!

WE'RE GOING TO BUY TIME FOR OUR ARMY BY HOLDING THIS TOWN!
TO HELL WITH YOU, MAJOR — I'M GONNA BREAK YOUR BACK!
DOWN, BIG MAN — YOU'LL DO WHAT I SAY!
YAHHHHHHHHHHH!
GOTT — HE PUT MAX DOWN WITH THAT AMMO BOX!
HE'S DUCKIN' EVERYTHING! SOMEONE GET THAT MAJOR!
THE FLANKS ARE SLIPPERY! CAN'T GET A FOOTHOLD!
GREASE. . .HE'S COVERED THE TIGER FLANKS. WITH PANZER GREASE!
JA! NOW LISTEN TO ME, YOU PACK OF SCUM! IF YOU RUN AFTER OUR ARMIES YOU'LL GET SHOT AS DESERTERS. SURRENDER TO THE IVANS, AND YOU'LL GET A BULLET FROM THEM! YOUR ONLY CHANCE IS STAY AND FIGHT!
HEY — HE'S RIGHT!
YOU BET I'M RIGHT. WE MUST HOLD THIS TOWN FOR 24 HOURS AND I NEED A TANK CREW. YOU, BIG MAN, AND YOU, WITH THE DIRTY CAP!
JA, WE'RE TANKMEN.
OKAY, MAJOR, WE'RE WITH YOU.
"SO WE HELD THE TOWN OF OZEL, ONE CONVICT BATTALION AGAINST A WHOLE RUSSIAN SHOCK ARMY. WE HELD 'EM 'TILL WE GOT CUT DOWN, ONE BY ONE."
"THEN WE GOT THE BREAKOUT ORDER AND SLIPPED INTO THE SNOWS. WHEN WE GOT THROUGH TO OUR LINES, THERE WAS JUST US THREE LEFT."
HELLMAN JERKED HIS MEN'S THOUGHTS BACK TO THE PRESENT.
AND WE'RE STILL TOGETHER. TO THINK I STARTED THIS WAR WITH A PROUD PANZER REGIMENT — AND END UP LEADING A COUPLE OF GANGSTERS.
WE'RE THE BEST THERE IS, MAJOR. AN' YOU KNOW IT.
SHUT UP, MAX — LOOK! A STAFF CAR!

IT'S A GENERAL'S CAN – CAUGHT BY A RUSSIAN JABO, I'D SAY. GET THE GOLD BRAID AND THE SILVER CROSSES. . . AND THE DRINK.
GET YOUR DIRTY PAWS OFF THAT STUFF, YOU TWO! I THOUGHT I'D TAMED YOU OF YOUR LOOTING HABITS. LET'S GO!

THAT BORDER TOWN'S BEING EVACUATED. WE MAY AS WELL JOIN THE INFANTRY DOWN THERE.
HUH, FORCED TO FIGHT AS INFANTRY. WE'RE TRAINED TANKMEN!

BUT, AS THEY APPROACHED THE BURNING TOWN.
WELL, WELL, MAJOR IS BIG MAX GOING MAD OR IS THAT A TANK FACTORY?
YOU'RE MAD ALL RIGHT, BUT IT DOES LOOK LIKE NEW MACHINES IN THERE! LET'S SEE!
HENSCHEL
PANZER WERKE
A.G.

HALTE! THIS PLANT IS UNDER GUARD AGAINST LOOTERS – AND YOU THREE LOOK LIKE THE TYPE!
FIELD POLICE! BOY, DO I HATE WATCHDOGS!

LISTEN, LEUTNANT, I MAY LOOK ROUGH, BUT I'M A PANZER MAJOR AND I WANT A TANK TO FIGHT IN!
SORRY, MAJOR – NOBODY TOUCHES THOSE TANKS WITHOUT THE GENERAL'S PERMISSION!

LEUTNANT, THOSE MACHINES ARE STANDING IDLE AND THE RUSSIAN FRONT'S COMING THIS WAY!
SORRY, MAJOR – IF YOU ARE ONE. I HAVE MY ORDERS FROM THIS AREA COMMANDER, GENERAL VON BRAUN. NOW GET OUT OF HERE!

IF HE WEARS A MONOCLE, THEN WE'VE JUST SEEN HIM AND HE'S. . .
ER – COME AWAY, PLEASE HERR MAJOR. MAX AND I THINK WE CAN HELP.

ONCE THEY WERE OUT OF SIGHT.
THE GENERAL'S COAT – YOU TWO DID LOOT FROM HIM! YOU COUPLE OF. . .
EASY, SIR – DO YOU WANT A TANK OR NOT?

LATER.
YOU'RE BACK, YOU UNSHAVEN SCUM! WE WARNED YOU –
YOU SAID YOU TAKE YOUR ORDERS FROM THE GENERAL. WELL, HE'S ARRIVED AND IS TALKING TO OUR MAJOR!

THE MPS SNAPPED TO ATTENTION, SEEING THE IMPRESSIVE FIGURE NEARBY.
THE GENERAL!
AND HE'S GIVEN US AUTHORITY TO TAKE ONE OF THE TANKS. OR DO YOU WANT TO ARGUE WITH HIM?
VERY WELL, CARRY ON!
HMM, EEENY-MEENY-MINEY... HEY, DEKKER, WE GOT A CHOICE. MARK IVS, JAGDPANTHERS.
THAT ONE – THAT'S THE BEST!
A ROYAL TIGER... ALL READY FOR US WITH PLENTY OF FUEL AND AMMO!
BIG MAX, TRAINED DRIVER, TOUCHED THE STARTERS AND THE MASSIVE MAYBACH ENGINE ROARED INTO LIFE.
'SCUSE, PLEASE, WATCHDOGS! YOUR GENERAL WANTS US UP WITH HIM.
THEY'RE DRIVING OFF WITH THEIR MAJOR! S-SOMETHING IS WRONG. HERR GENERAL!
A SNOWMAN! THEY'VE TRICKED US!
HELLMAN, MAX UND DEKKER NACH RUSSISCH FRONT!
ALL ENQUIRIES TO THE RUSSIAN FRONT!.. THAT'S WHAT I WROTE, SIR.
AND THE RUSSIANS ARE COMING THIS WAY TOWARDS BERLIN. BUT WITH THIS BRUTE, MAYBE WE CAN BUY A BIT MORE TIME... IN THE BATTLE FOR GERMANY!
MORE EXCITING ACTION WITH MAJOR KURT HELLMAN NEXT ISSUE!

DESPERATELY TRYING TO BUY TIME... HELLMAN AND HIS CREW FACE THE RUSSIANS... ALONE!

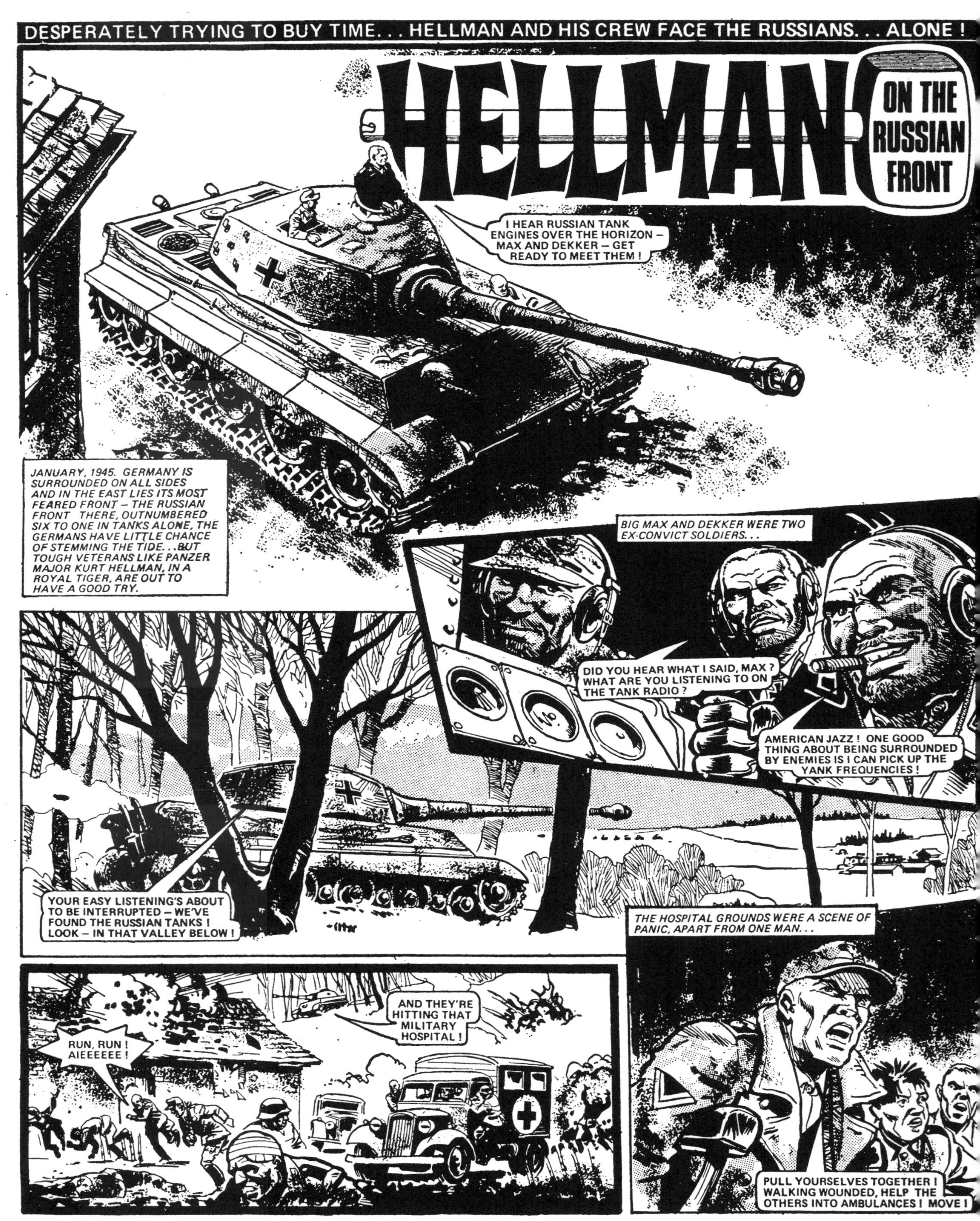
HELLMAN
ON THE RUSSIAN FRONT
I HEAR RUSSIAN TANK ENGINES OVER THE HORIZON – MAX AND DEKKER – GET READY TO MEET THEM!
JANUARY, 1945. GERMANY IS SURROUNDED ON ALL SIDES AND IN THE EAST LIES ITS MOST FEARED FRONT – THE RUSSIAN FRONT THERE, OUTNUMBERED SIX TO ONE IN TANKS ALONE, THE GERMANS HAVE LITTLE CHANCE OF STEMMING THE TIDE...BUT TOUGH VETERANS LIKE PANZER MAJOR KURT HELLMAN, IN A ROYAL TIGER, ARE OUT TO HAVE A GOOD TRY.
BIG MAX AND DEKKER WERE TWO EX-CONVICT SOLDIERS...
DID YOU HEAR WHAT I SAID, MAX? WHAT ARE YOU LISTENING TO ON THE TANK RADIO?
AMERICAN JAZZ! ONE GOOD THING ABOUT BEING SURROUNDED BY ENEMIES IS I CAN PICK UP THE YANK FREQUENCIES!
YOUR EASY LISTENING'S ABOUT TO BE INTERRUPTED – WE'VE FOUND THE RUSSIAN TANKS! LOOK – IN THAT VALLEY BELOW!
RUN, RUN! AIEEEEEE!
AND THEY'RE HITTING THAT MILITARY HOSPITAL!
THE HOSPITAL GROUNDS WERE A SCENE OF PANIC, APART FROM ONE MAN...
PULL YOURSELVES TOGETHER! WALKING WOUNDED, HELP THE OTHERS INTO AMBULANCES! MOVE!

HE ROYAL TIGER RUMBLED INTO
HE HOSPITAL GROUNDS...
THAT SERGEANT WAS SOMEHOW FAMILIAR – BUT I'VE NO TIME TO THINK WHY !
THE RUSSKIES AIN'T SEEN US YET, SIR – RECKON WE'VE A FEW SECONDS !
LAUNDRY
TIME TO SET UP A TRAP. DEKKER, YOU SEE THAT LAUNDRY AHEAD..?
ND...
GUT ! COVER THE TANK WITH THE WHITE SHEETS AND WE HAVE EXCELLENT CAMOUFLAGE !
YOU BET, MAJOR !
OKAY, ACTION STATIONS! I'LL COME DOWN AND HELP AS GUNLOADER !
ALL SET, SIR ! HERE THEY COME – A WHOLE TANK COMPANY !
LIKE A MOB OF PEASANTS !
FEUER !
NOW MEET THE KING !
EXT SECOND, TWO T34s
ERE ABLAZE...
AIEEEE !
ARMOURED LIKE A HEAVY CRUISER, THE TIGER II SHRUGGED OFF THE WAVE OF RUSSIAN TANK SHELLS...
PEASANTS ! THEY SHOULD KNOW YOU CAN'T TAKE A TIGER HEAD-ON !

KEEP FIRING, DEKKER – I'LL KEEP LOADING !
HUH – THREE MEN ARE NOT ENOUGH TO MAN A TIGER !
THEN...
ON, COMRADES – WE'LL TAKE THAT TIGER ON FOOT !
DA !
MAJOR – IVAN INFANTRY ON THE LEFT ! WE NEED A SPANDAU ON 'EM !
AND I'VE GOT TO KEEP FEEDING DEKKER ! WE'RE TOO MANY HANDS SHORT IN HERE !
ON, COMRADES – ONE FAST RUSH AND WE ARE ON THEM !
SUDDENLY...
AIEEEE !
HEY – SOMEONE'S TACKLIN' THOSE INFANTRY ON HIS OWN !
I DON'T BELIEVE IT ! HE'S GOT THEM ALL AND SEE WHO IT IS – THAT HOSPITAL SERGEANT !
AIEEEE !
HE MUST BE AS MAD AS US !
WHOEVER HE IS, HE'S DONE US A GOOD TURN ! MAX, TAKE US ALONGSIDE AND GET HIM ABOARD !
COME ON, CRIPPLE – GET IN !
DON'T TALK TO ME LIKE THAT, YOU TRAMP OF A PANZERMAN !

AS THE SERGEANT WAS HAULED IN. . .
I KNOW YOU! KESSEL – SERGEANT KESSEL! FROM THE EARLY DAYS ON THE RUSSIAN FRONT!
HELLMAN! MAJOR HELLMAN IT'S YOU! AFTER ALL THIS TIME!
LAST TIME WE SAW EACH OTHER WAS SPRING '43 – JUST BEFORE KURSK!
AND KURSK WAS WHERE MY LEG CAUGHT IT, SIR – THEN I WAS SENT BACK HOME TO THIS QUIET HOSPITAL.
BUT NOW WE MUST FALL BACK AND SET A NEW TRAP!
JA, MAJOR – WE WERE BOTH TRAINED TO SET TRAPS. . . REMEMBER?
LIKE YOU DID WITH YOUR CRUTCHES OUT THERE? YOU'RE MAD, CRIPPLE!
DON'T TALK TO ME LIKE THAT, JAILBIRD! JA – I SEE YOUR CONVICT FLASHES! GOTT, WHAT IS THE MAJOR DOING RIDING WITH SCUM LIKE YOU?
WATCH IT, SERGEANT CRIPPLE!
SHUT UP, ALL OF YOU! KESSEL, THESE MEN MAY BE ROUGH, BUT THEY'RE RUSSIAN FRONT FIGHTERS! AS GOOD AS YOU ONCE WERE!
WHAT DO YOU MEAN WERE, SIR? I SHOWED YOU I CAN STILL OPERATE OUT THERE, DIDN'T I?
THIS TANK IS SHORT-HANDED, SIR! IT WOULD HELP IF YOU HAD A GOOD MACHINE-GUNNER, WOULDN'T IT?
YOU MEAN – JOIN OUR TANK CREW? YOU?
ANYWAY, I CAN SEE YOU NEED SOME CLASS IN HERE! SMOKING CIGARS INSIDE A TANK AND LISTENING TO ENEMY STATIONS –
SHUT UP, CRIPPLE, AND CHECK YOUR GUNS IF YOU'RE GONNA STAY!
JA. . . ME! I DON'T NEED MY LEGS IN A TANK SEAT! IF YOU'D HAVE ME, SIR!
JA, KESSEL!
WELCOME ABOARD, KESSEL! WE'RE FIGHTING A LOSING WAR. . . SO MAYBE WE ARE MADMEN! BUT WE'VE GOT THIS MIGHTY TIGER TO FIGHT IN AND THERE'S NOTHING WORSE THAN A MADDENED BEAST!
MORE BLAZING BATTLE-ACTION WITH MAJOR KURT HELLMAN NEXT WEEK!

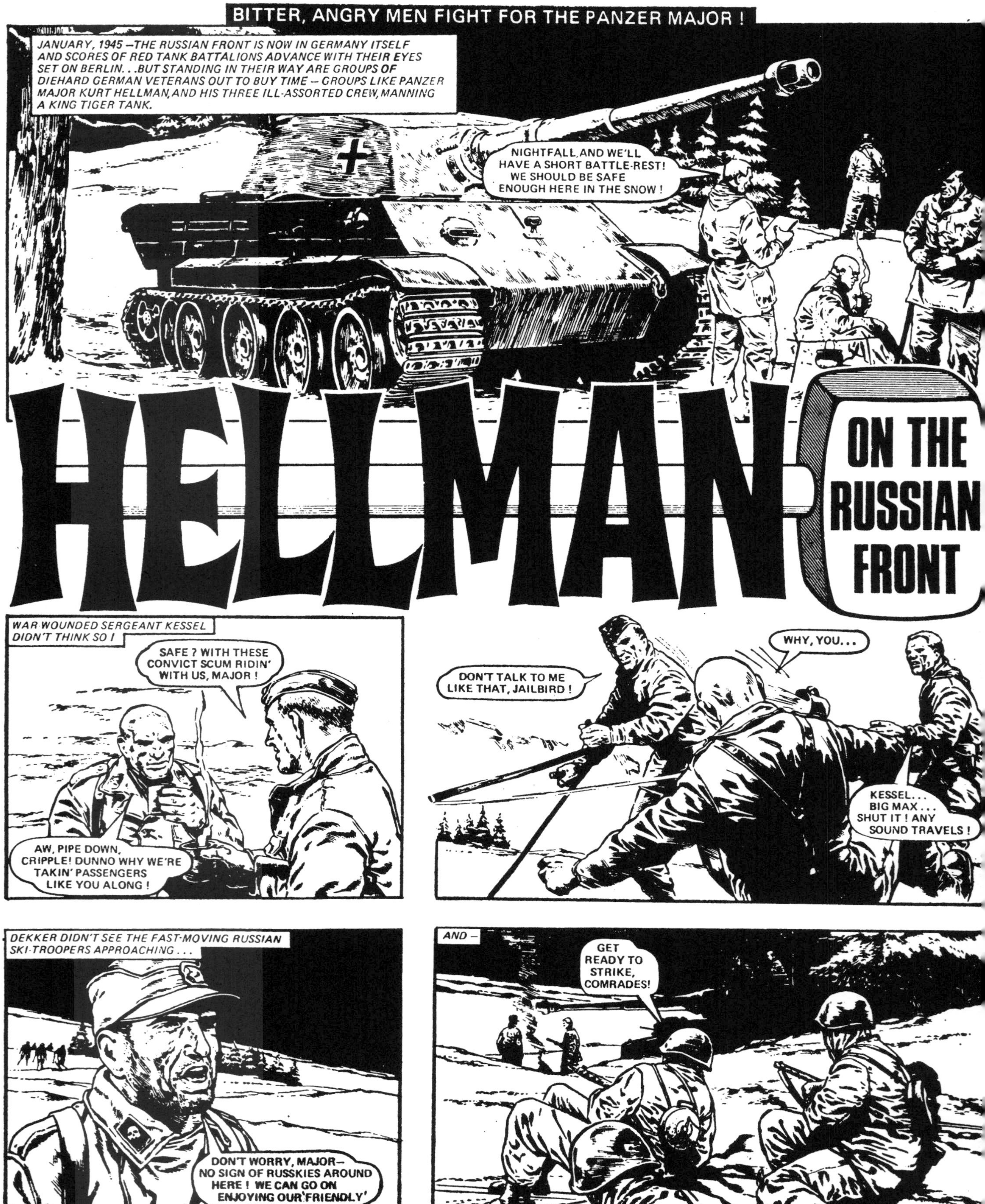

BITTER, ANGRY MEN FIGHT FOR THE PANZER MAJOR !

JANUARY, 1945 — THE RUSSIAN FRONT IS NOW IN GERMANY ITSELF AND SCORES OF RED TANK BATTALIONS ADVANCE WITH THEIR EYES SET ON BERLIN. . . BUT STANDING IN THEIR WAY ARE GROUPS OF DIEHARD GERMAN VETERANS OUT TO BUY TIME — GROUPS LIKE PANZER MAJOR KURT HELLMAN, AND HIS THREE ILL-ASSORTED CREW, MANNING A KING TIGER TANK.

NIGHTFALL, AND WE'LL HAVE A SHORT BATTLE-REST! WE SHOULD BE SAFE ENOUGH HERE IN THE SNOW !

HELLMAN ON THE RUSSIAN FRONT

WAR-WOUNDED SERGEANT KESSEL DIDN'T THINK SO !
SAFE ? WITH THESE CONVICT SCUM RIDIN' WITH US, MAJOR !
AW, PIPE DOWN, CRIPPLE! DUNNO WHY WE'RE TAKIN' PASSENGERS LIKE YOU ALONG !

DON'T TALK TO ME LIKE THAT, JAILBIRD !
WHY, YOU . . .
KESSEL . . . BIG MAX . . . SHUT IT ! ANY SOUND TRAVELS !

DEKKER DIDN'T SEE THE FAST-MOVING RUSSIAN SKI-TROOPERS APPROACHING . . .
DON'T WORRY, MAJOR— NO SIGN OF RUSSKIES AROUND HERE ! WE CAN GO ON ENJOYING OUR 'FRIENDLY' MEAL !

AND —
GET READY TO STRIKE, COMRADES!

KRASNA!
GOTT-REDS! AND THEY'VE CAUGHT US OUT OF THE TANK!
BIG MAX MOVED IN A FLASH –
GIVE US THAT CRUTCH, CRIPPLE – I'LL TAKE HIM!
A MASSIVE THROW, AND...
AIEEEEE
GOTT! HE JUST BLEW UP! THEY'RE A SUICIDE SQUAD CARRYING PACKMINES ON THEIR BACKS TO TAKE US WITH THEM!
SO LET'S HELP THEM COMMIT SUICIDE!
KESSEL... HE'S REACHED THE TANK'S FORWARD MG!
THE MG 34 SPRAYED...
AIEEEEEE!
GOOD FOR THE CRIPPLE... HE'S TAKEN THEM ALL!
JA, AND MAYBE YOU'LL GET A BULLET IF YOU DON'T STOP CALLING ME CRIPPLE! AND YOU LOST ME A CRUTCH, BIG MAN!
OKAY... OKAY! I'LL MAKE SURE I GET ANOTHER ONE FOR YOU!
SHUT UP, BOTH OF YOU! WE'LL HAVE TO FIND A NEW HIDE BEFORE DAWN!
OON –
IF WE'D HAD AN EXTRA AN ON-GUARD THOSE IVAN SUICIDERS WOULD NEVER AVE GOT SO CLOSE! WE NEED A FIFTH MAN, MAJOR!
SOMETHING OUT THERE – VILLAGE AHEAD!
LOOKS DESERTED – THE LOCALS MUST HAVE FLED IN THE RUSH FROM THE RUSSIAN ADVANCE! CLOSE ON THAT SCHOOL BUILDING, MAX...
SUDDENLY –
ROCKET COMING AT US FROM THAT ROOF – SWERVE, MAX!

MISSED US! C'MON, DEKKER – LET'S GET THAT MOSCOW MANIAC UP THERE!
I'LL TAKE THE ROOF OUT FROM UNDER HIM!
HOLD IT – THAT WASN'T A RUSSIAN ROCKET!
IT WAS A PANZERFAUST! THE MAN UP THERE IS GERMAN!
AS HELLMAN JUMPED DOWN FROM THE TANK SCHMEISSER BULLETS STITCHED THE SNOW..
THE FOOL CAN'T SEE US CLEARLY . . . SO KEEP THE TIGER OUT OF 'FAUST RANGE WHILE I DEAL WITH HIM!
HELLMAN DUCKED INTO THE SCHOOL –
HE'S RIGHT ABOVE ME AND STILL SPRAYING THAT SCHMEISSER!
BUT –
DIRTY RUSSIAN TRICK . . .
HELL! HE'S GONNA BLAST ME – GOT TO STOP THAT GUN!
HELLMAN GRABBED AT A NEARBY STANDARD AND SWUNG . . .
GOT YOU, YOU GUN-HAPPY FOOL!
AAAAH! YOU . . . YOU WON'T TAKE ME WITHOUT A FIGHT, RUSSIAN!
AND NO DAGGERS! HOLD IT, KID – I'M A GERMAN PANZER MAJOR!
ACH – I DIDN'T KNOW THERE WERE ANY FIGHTERS BUT ME LEFT AROUND HERE!

A, I AM HANS HEILER, CTION LEADER OF THE LOCAL HITLER YOUTH! L THE OTHER COWARDS HAVE FLED!
I THINK YOU HAD BETTER JOIN MY TANK! KNOW ANYTHING ABOUT THEM?
88MM GUN, FRONTAL ARMOUR 100MM, MAYBACH V-12 ENGINE, SHELL AMMO—THIRTY ROUNDS!
OKAY, SO YOU'VE READ UP. WE'LL NEED YOU ON THE SHELLS!
SO THAT'S OUR TANK KILLER—A KID!
I'M SIXTEEN SOON, BIG MAN, AND WATCH OUT! YOU'RE RUNNING OVER MY SILVER STANDARD!
HUH?
TWISTED AND SMASHED! YOU FOOL! THIS WAS A STANDARD BLESSED BY THE FUHRER HIMSELF!
YEAH! AN' I GOT A USE FOR THAT!
SEE—IT CAN BE A NEW CRUTCH FOR YOU, CRIPPLE! HOW'S THAT?
NOT BAD, JAILBIRD—IT'LL DO!
HOW DARE YOU—WHAT ARE YOUR NAMES?
HEY, THAT KID'S GOT A REPORT CARD!
I SHALL REPORT YOU BOTH FOR THIS INSULT TO THE PARTY!
KEEP THE CRUTCH, CRIPPLE—MAYBE OUR NEW ADDITION'S GONNA BE EVEN MORE ANNOYIN' THAN YOU!
JA—MAYBE YOU'RE RIGHT, JAILBIRD! SOUNDS A REAL LITTLE HITLER!
I HEARD THAT—ANOTHER INSULT TO THE FUHRER! YOUR NAMES ARE GOING INTO MY BOOK AGAIN AND WHEN WE REACH THE NEAREST PARTY HQ...
QUIET, NEW MAN. DON THE TANKSUIT AND GET TO YOUR DUTIES! YOU'RE GUNLOADER—SO CHECK THE SHELL STOCKS!
JA, HE'S A LITTLE HITLER RIGHT ENOUGH! TWO CONVICTS, A CRIPPLE, AND NOW A FANATIC KID COMPLETES MY CREW... BUT LET'S SEE HOW HE PULLS HIS WEIGHT AS A PANZER FIGHTER WHEN THE RUSSIANS COME!

HOW WILL HELLMAN'S LATEST RECRUIT FIT IN? DON'T MISS NEXT WEEK'S INSTALMENT!

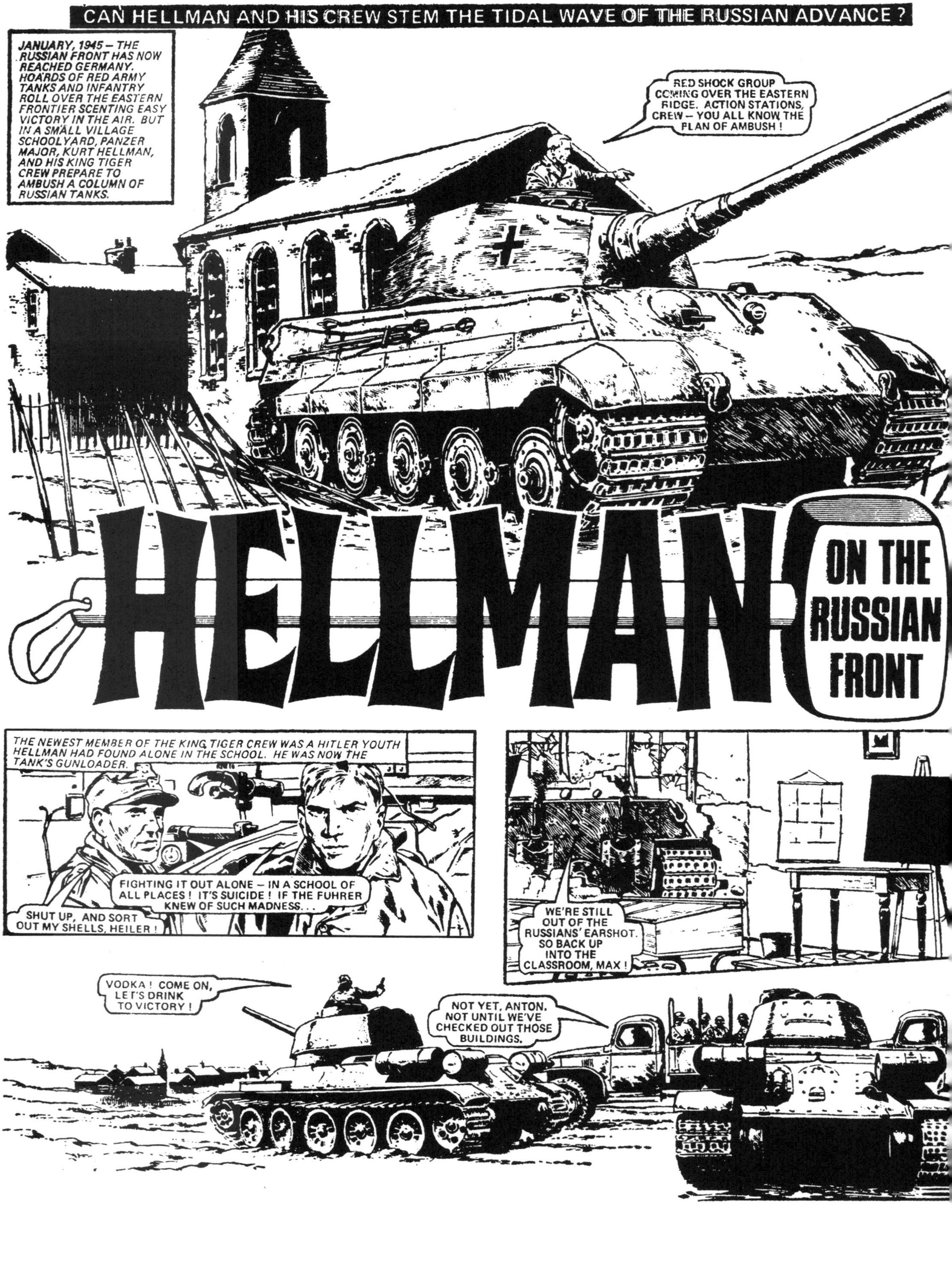

CAN HELLMAN AND HIS CREW STEM THE TIDAL WAVE OF THE RUSSIAN ADVANCE ?

HELLMAN ON THE RUSSIAN FRONT

JANUARY, 1945 – THE RUSSIAN FRONT HAS NOW REACHED GERMANY. HOARDS OF RED ARMY TANKS AND INFANTRY ROLL OVER THE EASTERN FRONTIER SCENTING EASY VICTORY IN THE AIR. BUT IN A SMALL VILLAGE SCHOOLYARD, PANZER MAJOR, KURT HELLMAN, AND HIS KING TIGER CREW PREPARE TO AMBUSH A COLUMN OF RUSSIAN TANKS.

RED SHOCK GROUP COMING OVER THE EASTERN RIDGE. ACTION STATIONS, CREW – YOU ALL KNOW THE PLAN OF AMBUSH !

THE NEWEST MEMBER OF THE KING TIGER CREW WAS A HITLER YOUTH HELLMAN HAD FOUND ALONE IN THE SCHOOL. HE WAS NOW THE TANK'S GUNLOADER.
FIGHTING IT OUT ALONE – IN A SCHOOL OF ALL PLACES ! IT'S SUICIDE ! IF THE FUHRER KNEW OF SUCH MADNESS. . .
SHUT UP, AND SORT OUT MY SHELLS, HEILER !

WE'RE STILL OUT OF THE RUSSIANS' EARSHOT. SO BACK UP INTO THE CLASSROOM, MAX !

VODKA ! COME ON, LET'S DRINK TO VICTORY !
NOT YET, ANTON. NOT UNTIL WE'VE CHECKED OUT THOSE BUILDINGS.

A SCHOOL, HA ! WE GIVE THE NAZIS THE LESSONS NOW, EH, KRASNOV ?
WRONG, RUSSKIE !
YOU'VE STILL GOT A FEW THINGS TO LEARN FROM US !
KAZANA ! IN THAT CLASSROOM...
GUNNER DEKKER AND THE DRIVER, BIG MAX, WERE EX-CONVICTS FROM THE SAME PENAL BATTALION.
COME ON, MAX, KEEP SCORE FOR ME !
THAT'S ONE OF THE SCUM OUT OF IT, MY FRIEND.
AND THAT'S TWO !
INFANTRY ! CLOSE ON THAT TANK !
BUT HELLMAN WAS READY FOR THE SHOCK TROOPS...
PANZERS DON'T DIE EASY, FRIENDS ! OKAY, MAX, GET THIS BEAST MOVING !
PERMISSION TO LEAVE THE ROOM, SIR ?
CUT OUT THE JOKES AND GET GOING — OUT THROUGH THE OPPOSITE WALL !
THE MIGHTY 150mm THICK FRONTAL ARMOUR SMASHED THROUGH THE WALL INTO THE SCHOOLYARD.
NICE THING ABOUT TANKS, KID, YOU REALLY CAN TAKE 'EM ANYWHERE !

AND ANOTHER ONE DOWN. NICE WORK, DEKKER. AND THE INFANTRY'S MAKING A RUN FOR IT! BERLIN IS SAFE A LITTLE LONGER.

JA – AND OLD ADOLF HITLER CAN SLEEP EASY ANOTHER NIGHT – WORSE LUCK!

YOUNG HEILER, THE LOADER, WAS KEEPING A REPORT-BOOK ON THE REST OF THE CREW'S ANTI-NAZI COMMENTS.

THAT'S THE THIRD BLACK MARK AGAINST YOU, BIG MAN. WHEN WE REACH A PARTY OFFICE I'LL MAKE SURE YOU ARE ARRESTED!

SHUDDUP KID.

THE KID MAY BE A PAIN IN THE NECK, SIR, BUT HE KNOWS A LOADER'S JOB ALL RIGHT.

JA – HE'S READ UP EVERY ARMY MANUAL AND WAS DUE TO JOIN UP THIS MONTH.

OKAY, OUR ARMY'S SCATTERED, AND THE FRONT'S COLLAPSED! WE'VE GOT TO PULL BACK FAST AND FIND ANOTHER AMBUSH HIDE!

ONE HOUR LATER...

THERE'S THE PRUSSIAN HIGHWAY. BUT THERE ARE ALSO CIVILIAN VEHICLES ON IT – GERMAN REFUGEES TRYING TO GET WEST. LOOKS LIKE A SCHOOL BUS IS BLOCKING THE ROUTE.

STUPID SCHOOLKIDS! WHO CARES ABOUT THEM. WE'RE FIGHTING TANKMEN – WE CAN'T LET THEM HOLD US UP!
HEY! OUR LITTLE HITLER LOOKS PALE ALL OF A SUDDEN.

AH, MAJOR! WE'RE STUCK IN THIS SNOW. CAN YOU HELP?
STAND CLEAR AND WE'LL GIVE YOU A PUSH.

THE POWERFUL MAYBACH ENGINES GENTLY EASED THE BUS BACK ON TO THE ROAD.
HE'S DONE IT!
WUNDERBAR! I AM THE SCHOOL'S HEAD-MASTER AND I THANK YOU, MAJOR.

UT WHEN THE SCHOOLMASTER GLANCED INTO THE REW HATCH...
JA – GOOD LUCK TO . . .MEIN GOTT ! HEILER ! MAJOR, THIS BOY DISAPPEARED WHEN WE WERE EVACUATING THE SCHOOL...
SO HE'S JUST A SCHOOL-BOY ! BUT HE TOLD US HE WAS SEVENTEEN !
HEILER SEVENTEEN ? NEIN, HE'S NOT FIFTEEN YET !
OKAY, BOY, OUT YOU GET AND JOIN THE BUS PARTY. COME ON. . .MOVE !
BUT, SIR...
I SAID OUT. I'M NOT GOING TO BE RESPONSIBLE FOR YOUR DEATH.
UT AT THAT MOMENT...
AND WHEN WE GET TO SAFETY... AIEEEEEEE !
GOTT – SHELLFIRE ! AND IT'S RANGED ON THE ROAD !
LOOK, SIR ! STALIN TANKS – UNCLE JOE'S OWN ! THEY'LL MASSACRE THESE REFUGEES !
NOT WITH US HERE, DEKKER. ACTION STATIONS ! CLOSE HATCHES ! SWING HER ROUND, MAX !
A BADLY SHAKEN HEILER CLIMBED BACK ON TO THE TANK.
STILL WITH US, EH, KID ?
MAJOR, SIR, IT'S A DEATH TRAP OUT HERE ! PLEASE LET ME IN. YOU'LL NEED EVERY PAIR OF HANDS NOW !
I'VE NO CHOICE. RIGHT, BACK TO YOUR STATION, HEILER.
HELLMAN SQUINTED THROUGH THE COMMANDER'S PERISCOPE.
YES. . JS3s. THE BEST TANKS IN THE RED ARMY. MAYBE THIS IS WHERE THE RUSSIAN FRONT ENDS FOR HELLMAN AND HIS CREW !
FOUR AGAINST ONE ! ARE THE ODDS TOO HIGH ? SEE NEXT WEEK !

AGAINST ALL ODDS. . .HELLMAN HAS TO BUY TIME FOR REFUGEES!
JANUARY, 1945 — THE BEGINNING OF THE END FOR GERMANY WITH THE RUSSIAN ARMIES ROLLING OVER ITS EASTERN FRONTIER WITH A SUPERIORITY OF SIX TO ONE. BUT STILL PANZER VETERANS FIGHT — MEN LIKE MAJOR KURT HELLMAN AND HIS KING TIGER CREW WHO ARE ABOUT TO TAKE ON A PACK OF STALIN TANKS!
IT'S US AGAINST FOUR UNCLE JOES! LET'S GO MEET 'EM!
WE'VE GOT TO BUY TIME FOR THE REFUGEE COLUMN!
HELLMAN
ON THE RUSSIAN FRONT
AMONG THE REFUGEE COLUMN WAS A SCHOOL BUS—
GOOD LUCK, TIGERMEN!
AND OUR SCHOOL MATE HEILER FIGHTS WITH THEM.
HELLMAN'S LOADER WAS, IN FACT, A SCHOOLBOY WHO'D LIED ABOUT HIS AGE.
YOU'D BETTER BE FAST PASSING ME THE SHELLS, HEILER!
YOU DO YOUR JOB— I'LL DO MINE, DEKKER!
SHUT UP, THE PAIR OF YOU AND GET THE 88 TALKING!
AIEEEE!
FIRE! FIRE!
WITH MASSIVE ARMOUR AND THE 88MM GUN, THE KING TIGER WAS STILL AT THAT TIME THE MOST POWERFUL DEFENCE TANK IN THE WORLD!

TOOK OUT ONE AND THE OTHERS ARE FIRIN' BACK! BUT THEY DON'T CUT UP THE KING!
WATCH OUT — HORN SOUNDING BEHIND US!
THE COACH—THEY'RE WARNING US! TWO MORE STALINS HAVE GOT ON TO THE HIGHWAY BEHIND US!
WATCH OUT — WATCH OUT, TIGERMEN!
THANKS, DRIVER — NOW GET YOUR BUS OUT OF HERE!
TOO LATE, MAJOR— ONE OF THE STALINS IS RACING IN TO RAM IT!
AIEEEEEE!
THEN—
THE DIRTY REDS ARE CLOSING IN FOR THE KILL! WE CAN'T FIGHT THEM ALL AT ONCE!
STAVA STALINO! ALL GUNS FIRE!
HELLMAN LEAPT FROM HIS COMMANDER'S SEAT—
ARMOUR-PIERCING SHELLS COMING AT HEAD-HEIGHT! HIT THE DECK!
YAHHHHHH!
WHEWW — ANOTHER INCH AND I'D HAVE HAD AN EVEN WORSE CREWCUT!
JA, THEY'VE MISSED OUR HEADS BUT THEY'VE GOT OUR TANK AT LAST!
THE TIGER'S FLANKS AND REAR WERE ITS WEAK SPOTS!
BURNING BOTH SIDES, SIR — THIS KING'S ALMOST HAD IT!
LET'S SEE WHAT'S WAITING FOR US IF WE BALE OUT...

AS THE CRIPPLED SERGEANT KESSEL PRODDED AT THE HATCH WITH HIS CRUTCH —
YAHH — A WALL OF MG FIRE, THAT'S WHAT! NO PRISONER-TAKING! THEY WANT US TO STAY IN HERE AND BURN ALIVE!
SO WHAT DO WE DO NOW, MAJOR?

THE FIRE HASN'T REACHED OUR ENGINE OR TRANSMISSION YET! SWING US ROUND AND HEAD FOR THAT BUS-WRECK BACK ON THE ROAD!
YOU BET, MAJOR!

HA. . STILL THE GERMAN FOOLS TRY TO RUN FOR IT!
WE WILL CRUSH THEM— LIKE WE DID THE BUS!

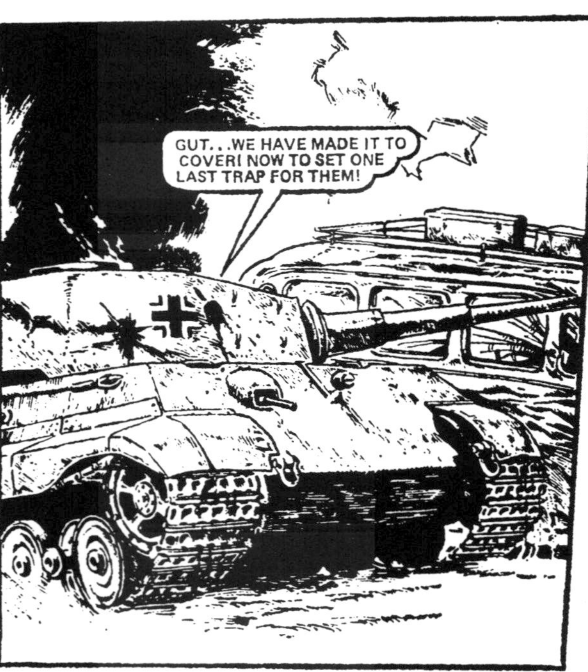

GUT. . . WE HAVE MADE IT TO COVER! NOW TO SET ONE LAST TRAP FOR THEM!

BALE OUT! EVERYONE SHELTER BEHIND THE BUS!

HELLMAN HAD TAKEN OFF HIS PANZER SCARF. . .
WHAT ARE YOU GOING TO DO, MAJOR? SURELY YOU CANNOT SAVE US NOW!
STOP WHINING, BOY! OR I'LL THROW YOU TO THE REDS MYSELF!

HEY, GOGOL — IT IS SOVIET "STEAMROLLER" TIME!
DA — WE GO IN SIDE BY SIDE!

STAY PUT, BOY!
NO! NO! WE'LL BE CRUSHED!

THE STALIN TANKS BEGAN TO ROLL OVER THE WRECK —
EIGHTY TONS OF STALIN, GERMANSKI — NOW SCREAM UNDER OUR WHEELS!
I HAVE SOAKED MY SCARF IN PETROL, MAX. .

NEXT SECOND, THE BUS EXPLODED! AND...
...SO NOW LET'S TAKE THE STEAM OUT OF THEM WITH A BURNING RAG AND AN OPEN PETROL HATCH!
GOT YOU, MAJOR!
BACK – EVERYONE!
AIEEEEEE!
AS THE RUSSIANS TRIED TO ESCAPE FROM THEIR BURNING TANKS –
IT'S NOT HEALTHY TO FIGHT OUT IN THE OPEN, EH, COMRADES!
AIEEEEE!
GOT 'EM ALL! HEY – IS THAT HEILER UP THERE?
SIR, THE KID HAS CLAMBERED BACK INTO OUR BURNING TIGER!
HELLMAN SPRANG FOR THE TANK AND, JUST IN TIME, YANKED THE YOUTH CLEAR...
...HAD TO RETRIEVE MY REPORT BOOK... AAAAAH!
STUPID, LITTLE FOOL! I OUGHT TO LET YOU BURN!
HEILER, AN ARDENT BELIEVER IN HITLER, WAS KEEPING A REPORT BOOK ON THE CREW'S ANTI-NAZI COMMENTS....
I'VE HEARD ALL YOUR FILTHY TALK ABOUT THE FUHRER, REMEMBER– AND, I STILL INTEND TO HAND IT IN TO THE NEAREST NAZI PARTY OFFICE!
THE WAY WE'RE BEING FLUNG BACK, YOU'LL SOON BE ABLE TO HAND IT IN TO ADOLF IN BERLIN ITSELF!
SOON, THE FIVE TANKMEN WERE HEADING WEST...
MY CREW MAY SNARL AT EACH OTHER BUT THEY'RE STILL IN ONE PIECE! NOW WE'RE RUNNING ON FOOT...SO HOW MUCH LONGER CAN WE FIGHT ON IN THIS DIRTY RUSSIAN WAR?
DON'T MISS NEXT WEEK'S THRILLING INSTALMENT ! ORDER YOUR COPY NOW !

FIVE TANK MEN AGAINST ALL KINDS OF DIRTY FIGHTING !

BIG BLIZZARD COMING - ENOUGH TO SLOW UP THE RED ADVANCE AND BUY US MORE TIME!
BUT WE NEED ANOTHER TANK TO FIGHT IN, HERR MAJOR!

JANUARY, 1945. THE SOVIET STEAMROLLER DRIVES DEEPER INTO GERMANY, LEAVING FEW THINGS STANDING IN ITS WAKE. BUT VETERAN MAJOR KURT HELLMAN AND HIS FOUR CREW MEMBERS, WHO HAVE BEEN FORCED TO BALE OUT OF THEIR KNOCKED OUT TANK, ARE STILL ON THEIR FEET AND READY TO FIGHT AGAIN!

BIG MAX AND DEKKER, THE CREW DRIVER AND GUNNER, WERE TWO EX-CONVICT TANKMEN FROM A GERMAN PENAL BATTALION
GOTTA GET OUT OF THIS COLD – I HATE IT!
ME, TOO – I AIN'T GONNA FREEZE TO DEATH LIKE OUR STUPID MATES DID AT STALINGRAD!
YOU DARE CALL THE HEROES OF STALINGRAD STUPID? THEY DID THEIR DUTY AND HELD THEIR GROUND!
JA – ALL BECAUSE OF ADOLF HITLER'S MAD ORDERS! THEY COULDA BROKEN OUT!

THIRD MEMBER OF THE CREW WAS A YOUTH NAMED HEILER, WHO BELIEVED FANATICALLY IN HITLER AND WAS KEEPING A REPORT BOOK ON THE OTHERS' ANTI-NAZI COMMENTS

THEN

DOWN, KID – ENEMY MOTORISED TROOPS AHEAD!

BUT THEY AIN'T RUSSIAN!

Hellman
ON THE RUSSIAN FRONT

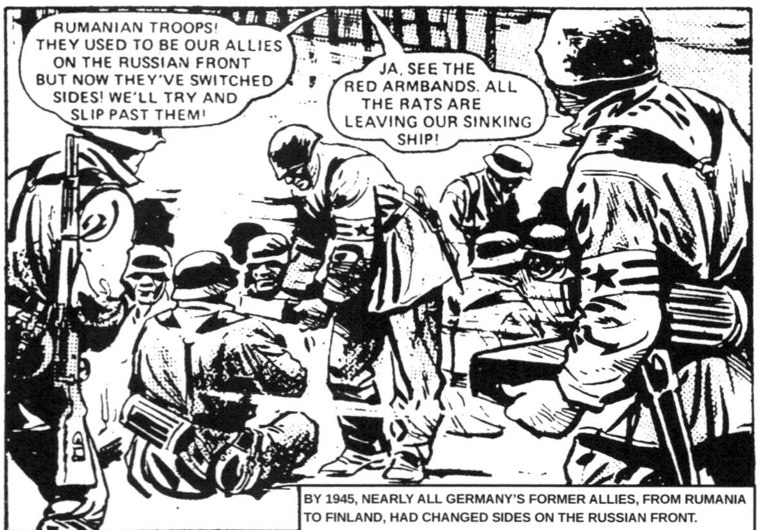
RUMANIAN TROOPS! THEY USED TO BE OUR ALLIES ON THE RUSSIAN FRONT BUT NOW THEY'VE SWITCHED SIDES! WE'LL TRY AND SLIP PAST THEM!
JA, SEE THE RED ARMBANDS. ALL THE RATS ARE LEAVING OUR SINKING SHIP!

BY 1945, NEARLY ALL GERMANY'S FORMER ALLIES, FROM RUMANIA TO FINLAND, HAD CHANGED SIDES ON THE RUSSIAN FRONT.

LATER
ANOTHER ENEMY POSITION TO GET PAST – HUNGARIAN THIS TIME! LUCKY FOR US THEY'RE KEEPING THEIR HEADS DOWN, TOO!

THE TURNCOAT SCUM ARE EVERYWHERE – BUT BEFORE STALINGRAD IT WAS DIFFERENT! WHAT I'D GIVE TO BE FIGHTING WITH THE PROUD GERMAN ARMY OF '41!

LOOK AHEAD – ANOTHER CAMP!
GERMAN VOICES AND FIGHTING IN PANTHERS! WE'VE REACHED OUR OWN KIND AT LAST!
ACHTUNG!

WOW – SEE HOW THEY SPRANG TO ATTENTION AND LOOK HOW SMART THEY ARE ! THEY'RE HOW GERMAN SOLDIERS SHOULD BE!
AND LOOK AT THEIR MACHINES! WHAT I'D GIVE TO GET MY HANDS ON ONE!

GRUKEN! MAJOR HELLMAN AND CREW! MIND IF WE SHARE YOUR FIRE? WE'VE BEEN ON THE MOVE SINCE OUR TIGER WAS KNOCKED OUT!
WE'RE LOOKING FOR A NEW MACHINE, SIR – KNOW OF ANY TANK DEPOTS STILL OPERATING IN THE AREA?

SORRY, I CAN'T HELP YOU! WE'RE JUST MOVING UP TO THE FRONT AGAIN.
I'LL BET YOU ARE, SIR. AND I BET YOU'VE SEEN ACTION EVERYWHERE!

GOOD HUNTING!
JA, MAJOR – BECAUSE YOU ARE THE HUNTED! ANOTHER FIVE YARDS AND WE TURN THE TURRET AND KILL YOU AND YOUR RUFFIANS!

UT. SUDDENLY –
HEY – THE KID'S RUNNING AFTER US!
PLEASE, SIR – PLEASE TAKE ME WITH YOUR TANK TROOP!

PLEASE, SIR – LET ME JOIN YOU, SIR! I WANT TO BE AMONG MEN WHO REALLY ACT LIKE GERMAN SOLDIERS!
GET OFF . . . GET OFF, YOU LITTLE SLUG!

HEY – SEE WHAT HE'S WEARING UNDER HIS COMBAT JACKET!
A RED ARMBAND!

HELLMAN YELLED –
THEY'RE SEIDLITZERS! RENEGADES WORKING FOR THE REDS!
THEY'RE ONTO US! TURN AND WIPE THEM OUT!

BUT BIG MAX AND DEKKER MOVED FASTER!
GRENADE BUNDLES – INTO THE TURRET RING!

AIEEEEEEEEEE!
THE SCHWEIN – WIPE THEM OUT! CLOSE HATCHES! CLOSE HATCHES!

BUT HELLMAN HAD LEAPT FOR THE OTHER PANTHER'S BLIND SIDE . . .
TOO SLOW, SEIDLITZER!

BUT I'LL MAKE IT A QUICK END FOR YOU!
AIEEEEEEEE!

BUT THE TANK COMMANDER HAD LEAPT FROM THE TURRET . . .
YOU, LITTLE SLUG – YOU GAVE US AWAY! I'LL BLAST YOUR HEAD OFF YOUR NECK FOR THAT!

THE CRIPPLED SERGEANT KESSEL SPRANG FROM COVER - AND . . .
NO, SEIDLIZTER – YOU'RE THE ONE TO GET IT IN THE NECK!
URGGHHHHH!

THOSE SMART GERMANS WERE FROM THE SEIDLITZ DIVISION, HEILER – GERMANS CAPTURED AT STALINGRAD WHO'VE JOINED THE RED SIDE! THEY WERE SENT IN TO INFILTRATE OUR LINES IN CAPTURED PANTHERS!
YEH, AND NOW THEY'RE BOTH BURNING HEAPS! WHAT A WASTE OF GOOD GERMAN TANKS!

JA – WE'RE STILL WITHOUT WHEELS AND WE'VE GOT ENEMIES ALL AROUND US! BUT IF WE ARE TO FIGHT AGAIN, THEN WE MUST FIND OURSELVES A TANK, OR WE ARE FINISHED FOR GOOD ON THE RUSSIAN FRONT!

NEXT WEEK – HELLMAN AND HIS CREW GET INVOLVED IN A TANK BATTLE. . . ON FOOT !

HELLMAN JOINS THE RUSSIAN ARMY — TO KILL A RUSSIAN TANK!

EARLY 1945. THE BEGINNING OF THE END FOR GERMANY WITH THE RUSSIANS ROLLING IN FROM THE EAST WITH THEIR MASSED FORCES AND FIREPOWER. BUT TRYING TO SLIP THROUGH THE FRONT AND TAKE PART IN THE LAST BATTLES, ARE THE BALED-OUT TANK CREW, LED BY THE VETERAN MAJOR, KURT HELLMAN.
WE'RE FALLING BACK ALONG THE BERLIN ROAD—BUT WE MUST FIND OURSELVES A NEW BATTLE TANK SOON!
ACH—WADIN' THROUGH DITCHWATER! I FEEL AS SMALL AN' DIRTY AS ADOLF HIMSELF!

AMONG THE CREW WAS THE YOUTH, HEILER, WHO FANATICALLY BELIEVED IN THE FÜHRER.
HERR MAJOR! THAT BIG CONVICT-SOLDIER JUST INSULTED OUR GLORIOUS LEADER AGAIN! I MUST RECORD IT IN MY BOOK!
PUT THE BOOK AWAY, BOY—I SEE SOMETHING MORE IMPORTANT! TANK FLASHES AHEAD!

HELLMAN ON THE RUSSIAN FRONT

HELLMAN AND HIS MEN EDGED FORWARD. AND —
A CROSSROADS—AND A LONE GERMAN PANTHER HOLDING IT AGAINST T34s AND INFANTRY!
JA, AND THOSE POOR PANTHERMEN HAVE GOT NOBODY ON FOOT TO HELP THEM!

BUT WE'RE ON FOOT! MAX AND DEKKER—I'M SURE YOU'RE CARRYING RUSSIAN CAPS AS SOUVENIRS!
FUNNY YOU SHOULD SAY THAT, SIR — WANT ONE?
AND—
HIMMEL—THE MAJOR IN A RUSSIAN CAP! IT IS WRONG OF A GERMAN COMMANDER TO . . .
QUIET, BOY—YOU STAY HERE WITH ME AND GIVE COVER! HELP ME SET UP THE M.G.!

A GROUP OF RUSSIAN INFANTRY WERE ALREADY STALKING THE PANTHER . . .
WE'VE GOT BEHIND HIM! YOU MEN AT THE BACK—CLOSE UP! WE HIT IT ANY SECOND . . .
YOU HEARD THE COMRADE OFFICER, MAX!
JA, HIT THEM ANY SECOND!
NIET—AIEEEEEEEE!

NEARBY, HELLMAN HAD WORKED CLOSER TO A T34.
NEAR ENOUGH—NOW TO TRY FOR THAT OPEN TURRET HATCH WITH A COUPLE OF GRENADES!
STOI-SPIONE!
HELLMAN LOBBED THE GRENADES INTO THE TANK.
AIEEEEEE!
I'VE KILLED THAT T34! BUT ITS INFANTRY ARE OUT TO GET ME NOW!
BUT HELLMAN'S CRIPPLED SERGEANT WAS COVERING HIM...
MY CRUTCH IS GOOD SUPPORT FOR A MAN OR MACHINE-GUN, JA?
AIEEEEEEEE!
THE REMAINING T34s AT THE CROSSROADS SWIFTLY TURNED AWAY...
GOOD WORK, ALL OF YOU! NOW LET'S JOIN THE PANTHER CREW!
SOON THE TWO GERMAN GROUPS MET...
HAUPTMANN BRANDT, HERR MAJOR—THANKS FOR YOUR HELP!
Berlin K.
OUR PLEASURE, CAPTAIN. BUT WITH THAT HEAD WOUND YOU SHOULD NOT BE FIGHTING!
SUDDENLY—
A GERMAN JUNKERS TRANSPORT—AND ITS DROP DOORS ARE OPEN!
IT'S GOING TO DROP SUPPLIES! I TOLD YOU THE FUHRER HADN'T DESERTED US!
WRONG, BOY! THOSE AREN'T SUPPLIES THEY'RE DROPPING... THEY'RE HUNDREDS OF PROPAGANDA LEAFLETS!
SIGNED BY ADOLF HITLER HIMSELF AND INSTRUCTING EVERYONE ON THE FRONT TO FIGHT WHERE THEY STAND! ANYONE FOUND RETREATING WILL BE SHOT BY THE S.S.!
DAMN THEM! THEY WASTE VALUABLE AERO-FUEL DROPPING PAPER WHEN WE COULD BE GIVEN PETROL AND SHELL SPARES!

THE PLANE TURNED AWAY–
JA, YOU GET CLEAR OF THE FRONT AND SAFE BACK TO BERLIN, FLYBOYS! HOPE YOU CRASHLAND ON THE LITTLE MAN'S BUNKER!
HOW DARE YOU!
QUIET, BOY!
BUT, HERR MAJOR–ALL THESE MEN AROUND US–THEY'RE TALKING TREASON! IT'S MY DUTY TO REPORT THEM!
RIGHT NOW YOUR DUTY'S TO HELP HOLD THIS STRONG POINT! GRAB A TRENCH-TOOL! WE'RE GOING TO DIG AN ANTI-TANK DITCH.
I HOPE THAT LITTLE LUNATIC OF YOURS WAKENS UP TO WHAT'S HAPPENING IN GERMANY!
JA–AND I HOPE HE WON'T LEARN TOO LATE, SIR!
AT DUSK–
FINISHED THE DITCH–THOSE REDS WON'T GET OVER THIS CROSS-ROADS EASILY!
NOW TO GET TO MY BOOK.
HEILER, PUT THE BOOK AWAY! I'VE STILL WORK FOR YOU!
YOU'LL TAKE FIRST SENTRY DUTY TILL MIDNIGHT. GUARD THE SECTOR SOUTH AND EAST AND KEEP YOUR EYES PEELED FOR RUSSIANS! GOT IT?
YES, SIR!
BUT LATER–
THEY ARE ALL ASLEEP AND I'VE MEMORISED THEIR EVERY WORD AGAINST THE FUHRER. NOTHING TO BE SEEN SOUTH AND EAST–I'M LEAVING MY POST!
HEILER CRAWLED TO HIS BOOK.
I MUST WRITE A REPORT. WAIT–SOMETHING MOVING TO THE EAST!
HEILER LOOKED ACROSS THE SNOW . . .
DISTANT AIRCRAFT–MUST BE THE TRANSPORT AGAIN, DROPPING MORE OF THE FUHRER'S MESSAGE! THE OTHER SENTRY HASN'T SEEN IT AND I'VE GOT MORE IMPORTANT THINGS TO DO THAN WATCH THE SNOWS!
BUT, A FEW MILES AWAY, TOUGH RUSSIAN AIRBORNE COMMANDOS WERE JUMPING FROM A DC3 INTO THE SNOWDRIFTS . . .
LEAP FOR THE SNOWS, AIR COMMANDOS! THOSE GERMAN-HELD CROSSROADS MUST BE TAKEN TO CLEAR THE WAY TO BERLIN! ALL WE NEED IS ONE WEAK SENTRY THEN WE CAN SLAUGHTER THEM AS THEY SLEEP!

DEATH HAS DROPPED FROM THE NIGHT SKY! READ ON NEXT WEEK!

AS HELLMAN'S CREW SLEEP... THE WINTER SNOWS COME ALIVE WITH RUSSIANS!

GERMANY, EARLY 1945. ITS SOLDIERS NOW FIGHT ON THE FATHERLAND'S SOIL, KNOWING THEIR DESPERATE BATTLE CAN NO LONGER BUY VICTORY...ONLY TIME! HOLDING A CROSSROADS WITH A SCRATCH FORCE, PANZER MAJOR KURT HELLMAN HAS WON ANOTHER DAY – BUT NOW THE RUSSIANS ARE ATTACKING BY NIGHT!
DAVAI! THAT GERMAN POSITION STOPPED RED TANKS, BUT IT WILL NOT STOP THE RED AIR COMMANDOS! WE ONLY NEED ONE WEAK SENTRY – AND WE SLAUGHTER THEM ALL AS THEY SLEEP!

YOUNG HEILER OF HELLMAN'S CREW SHOULD HAVE BEEN ON SENTRY DUTY. BUT INSTEAD HE WAS WRITING IN HIS REPORT BOOK...
URGHHHHH!
THE OTHER MAN ON SENTRY DUTY WILL SPOT ANYTHING COMING ACROSS THE SNOWS. I MUST KEEP MY REPORT ON THESE ANTI-NAZIS UP TO DATE!

HELLMAN ON THE RUSSIAN FRONT

AN ARDENT BELIEVER IN HITLER, HEILER WAS KEEPING A REPORT OF ANY ANTI-NAZI COMMENTS HE HEARD.

ONLY MAJOR HELLMAN IS NOT IN MY BOOK. BUT ONE WORD AGAINST THE FUHRER – AND HIS NAME GOES DOWN, TOO!
HUH?
GOTT IN – URGHHH!
DAVAI – SLIT HIM SWIFTLY!

HELLMAN, AWAKENED BY THE BOOK, FOLLOWED UP FAST...
THE RUSSIANS ARE ALL OVER US! RAUS! RAUS! WAKE UP, EVERYONE!
URRAYUA! BLAST THEM WHERE THEY SLEEP!

BUT THE CRIPPLED SERGEANT KESSEL HAD BEEN SLEEPING WITH HIS TANK SPANDAU BESIDE HIM...
YOU GET THE BLASTING, RUSSIANS!
GOOD SHOOTING, CRIPPLE! BUT LEAVE SOME FOR BIG MAX AND DEKKER!

THE EX-CONVICTS, BIG MAX AND DEKKER, SWUNG INTO ACTION!
WUNDERBAR, SOLDIER! BUT CAN YOU GET OUR TANK INTO THE FIGHT?
YOU BET! DEKKER, WHERE ARE YOU?
COMING!
THERE ARE ONLY A HANDFUL OF THE GERMAN DEVILS! ATTACK WITH GRENADES!
SUDDENLY, THE SLEEK PANTHER TURRET SWUNG. AND...
AIEEEEEEE!
POW! POW! ACH, IT IS GREAT BEING BACK INSIDE A BATTLE TANK!
MOMENTS LATER–
YOUR TWO MEN HAVE WIPED OUT ALL THOSE COMMANDOS, MAJOR! BUT WILL THEY GIVE US OUR TANK BACK?
THEY WILL, CAPTAIN– OUT, YOU TWO! COME ON!
ACH–AFTER OUR GREAT BRAVERY, WE SHOULD GET THIS AS A PRESENT!
THE PANTHER BELONGED TO THE OTHER OFFICER AND HIS CREW, MUCH TO THE DISGUST OF BIG MAX AND DEKKER WHO'D BEEN LONGING FOR A NEW TANK SINCE THEIR OWN TIGER HAD BEEN KNOCKED OUT EARLIER.
HELLMAN TURNED TO THE SHAKEN HEILER...
AND YOU, BOY–YOU SHOULD HAVE SPOTTED THOSE RUSSIANS JUMPING FROM THEIR PLANE!
S-SORRY, MAJOR! I HEARD A PLANE BUT I THOUGHT IT WAS ANOTHER GERMAN ONE DROPPING MORE OF THESE PAMPHLETS!
THE GESTAPO PAMPHLETS WARNING US NOT TO RUN TO THE REAR BUT STAND AND FIGHT WHERE WE ARE! 'ACH, WE DON'T NEED STUPID MAIL LIKE THIS–WE NEED MORE AMMUNITION TO HOLD THESE CROSSROADS!
FIVE MILES BACK DOWN THE BERLIN ROAD, SIR–THERE'S A SUPPLY DUMP! WE COULD BE THERE AND BACK IN AN HOUR IN THE PANTHER!
AN HOUR, EH?
HELLMAN THOUGHT FAST–
OKAY–GET GOING! WE'LL STAY IN THIS POSITION UNTIL YOU RETURN WITH THE AMMO! BUT MAKE SURE YOU DO RETURN!
YOU CAN TRUST ME, SIR! MY CREW, GET ABOARD!
BIG MAX AND DEKKER WATCHED THE PANTHER TURN–
HEY, YOU SURE YOU DON'T WANT US TO TAKE IT OVER?
HA! OVER OUR DEAD BODIES! YOU CAN HAVE ALL THE AMMO WE'VE GOT LEFT, THOUGH!
SEE YOU SOON, MAJOR! IT'LL BE A PLEASURE TO FIGHT ALONGSIDE YOU AGAIN!

BUT THE FUHRER'S LEAFLETS FORBADE ANYONE TO LEAVE THEIR POSITIONS!
THEY'RE COMING BACK, HEILER! NOW GRAB A TRENCH TOOL—WE'RE GOING TO WIDEN OUR ANTI-TANK DITCH!

BUT, TWO HOURS LATER—
WE'VE MADE THE DITCH A LOT DEEPER, SIR. BUT THOSE BOYS AND THEIR PANTHER SHOULD BE BACK BY NOW!
JA, I WONDER WHAT'S KEEPING THEM? HEY, LISTEN! ENGINES TO THE EAST!

HEADLIGHTS—TANK HEADLIGHTS! AND I COUNT SIXTY, SEVENTY . . .
A WHOLE RED TANK DIVISION COMING THIS WAY! WHAT TARGETS THEY'D MAKE FOR JUST ONE OF OUR TANKS! WHERE IS THAT PANTHER?

BUT IT'S SUICIDE—JUST FIVE OF US FACING THEM! WE'LL HAVE TO MOVE BACK!
AT LEAST THE TANK DITCH WILL HOLD THEM UP HERE AT THE CROSSROADS. WE'VE DONE THAT MUCH!

WE'VE BEEN TOLD NOT TO MOVE, SIR! IT'S AGAINST THE FUHRER'S WISHES!
IF WE STAY HERE WE'LL BE MASSACRED! NOW MOVE IT!
HOLD ON, SIR — THIS CROSSROADS' SIGN . . .

. . . I'M BRINGIN' IT BACK WITH US! NOBODY CAN SAY NOW THAT WE STOPPED HOLDIN' THE CROSSROADS!
BUT WHY DIDN'T THE PANTHER COME BACK TO US? WE TRUSTED THAT CAPTAIN AND HIS CREW!

BUT SEVERAL MILES FURTHER ON . . .
SIR — THERE'S THE PANTHER AHEAD! STOPPED BY THAT GARAGE!
SOMETHING'S WRONG!

GOTT— THE CREWMEN ALL GUNNED DOWN AND . . .
. . . AND THE CAPTAIN'S BEEN HUNG FROM HIS TANK GUN!

POLITZEI
THE GESTAPO WERE IN WAIT HERE, WAITING FOR ANY GERMAN WHO CAME BACK ALONG THIS ROAD!
AND WAITING TO MURDER THEM! THE POOR GUYS COULDN'T EVEN DEFEND THEMSELVES . . . THEY LEFT THEIR AMMO WITH US!

SO NOW WE HAVE RUSSIANS TO OUR FRONT AND GERMAN BUTCHERS AT OUR BACKS! WE'RE BACK IN THE FIGHT FOR BERLIN WITH A TANK — BUT LET'S HOPE WE GET THE CHANCE TO SETTLE THE SCORE FOR OUR MURDERED COMRADES!

DON'T MISS NEXT WEEK'S THRILLING INSTALMENT ! ORDER YOUR COPY NOW !

HELLMAN ROARS INTO BATTLE – TO FIGHT GERMAN TROOPS !

GERMANY, EARLY 1945. NOT ONLY DO ITS SOLDIERS FACE OVERWHELMING ODDS ON ALL FRONTS – THEY HAVE THE NAZI BATTLE-POLICE AT THEIR BACKS. THE SS ARE MURDERING MEN WHO COME OUT OF THE FIGHTING LINE FOR ANY REASON. MAJOR KURT HELLMAN AND HIS TANK CREW HAVE COME UPON SUCH A MASSACRE AT A GERMAN SUPPLY GARAGE.
THESE MEN WERE HEROES... YET THEY WERE HUNG AND BUTCHERED BY THE SS BECAUSE THEY FELL BACK TO FIND SUPPLIES !
THE KILLER COPS HAVE GONE THEMSELVES, MAJOR HELLMAN !

JA – THE SS KNOW THE RUSSIANS ARE GOING TO ADVANCE ALONG THIS ROAD AND THEY DON'T WANT TO FACE THEM ! BUT AS THE MURDERERS RUN THEY SENSELESSLY KILL THEIR OWN COUNTRYMEN !

HELLMAN ON THE RUSSIAN FRONT

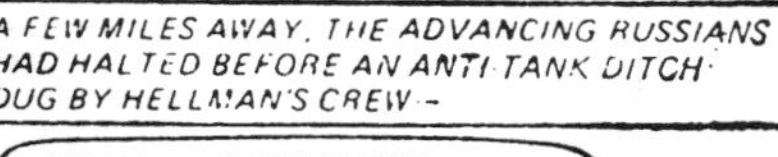

A FEW MILES AWAY, THE ADVANCING RUSSIANS HAD HALTED BEFORE AN ANTI-TANK DITCH DUG BY HELLMAN'S CREW –
STAVA – WE WANT THIS DITCH FILLED IN! BRING FORWARD THOSE GERMAN PRISONERS!
DAVI – NEMTSY !

FILL IN THAT DITCH! MOVE – MOVE !
JA – JA!

BACK AT THE PETROL STATION, BIG MAX AND DEKKER, BOTH EX-CONVICTS, WERE PREPARING SOME DIRTY TRAPS –
WE'LL LEAVE A FEW SURPRISES FOR UNCLE JOE'S BOYS !
JA – OUR FUEL TANKS ARE FULL – WE CAN GIVE THE REST TO THE RUSSIANS !

AT THE DITCH –
THE DITCH IS FILLED IN FOR YOU, SIR !
YES – AND NOW YOU ARE NO LONGER NEEDED. I CANNOT SPARE TIME TO TAKE PRISONERS!
OPEN FIRE !

NEIN — BITTE!
NO MERCY, GERMANS -- AND SOON THERE WILL BE A RUSSIAN BULLET FOR ADOLF HIMSELF!
AT TOP SPEED OF NEARLY 40 MPH, THE T 34S RACED ON –
PASS ROUND THE VODKA! THE ROAD TO BERLIN IS CLEAR!
KAMANDAIR — THE ROAD AHEAD IS FLOODED!
FLOODED WITH PETROL! THE GERMANS MUST BE FINISHED TO WASTE THEIR FUEL LIKE THIS!
LOOK — WIRES ACROSS THE ROAD! IT MUST BE A BOOBY-TRAP
JUST THEN, THE GRENADES EXPLODED –
AIEEEEE!
BALE OUT! INTO THE DITCH!
BUT . . .
NIET! STAKES — WOODEN STAKES!
AAHHEEEE!
SOME WAY AHEAD –
LOOKS LIKE OUR BOOBY TRAPS HAVE WORKED!
AT LEAST THEY GOT FAST SERVICE AT THE FILLING STATION!
OKAY, LET'S KEEP MOVING BACK! WE'VE GOT TO FIND SOME AMMO!
A FEW MILES LATER
TROUBLE AHEAD! POLICE MOTORBIKES AND SOME AMMO TRUCKS! SS HEADHUNTERS HAVE STOPPED MORE SUPPLY STRAGGLERS!
THEY'VE GOT THE ROPES OUT — BUT THERE'LL BE NO LYNCH PARTIES WHILE WE'RE AROUND! MAX — TAKE OUR MACHINE IN!
YOUNG HEILER, THE TANK'S GUN LOADER, WAS ALSO A HITLER FANATIC --
NEIN — THOSE SS ARE CARRYING OUT THE FUHRER'S ORDERS! LET ME OUT!
STAY PUT, KID!

NEXT SECOND –
OKAY, MAX. . .MAKE THEM JUMP ! BUT NO MURDER . . . HEAR ME ?
I HEAR YOU, MAJOR !
HALTE – NEIN, NEIN !
44 TONS OF PANTHER TORE INTO THE POLICE ROADBLOCK.
GOTT IN. . !
THE DIRTY. . !
AND –
HA – LOOK AT THEM FLEE! TELL HITLER IT WAS MAJOR HELLMAN'S CREW WHO STOPPED YOU SS MURDERERS THIS TIME!
BETTER NOT RUN, YOU RATS ! YOU'LL GET YOURSELVES ARRESTED!
NEARBY –
DIRTY, KILLER-COP! WE'LL DO THE EXECUTING NOW!
NEIN – HELP! HELP !
BUT HELLMAN STRODE FORWARD –
LEAVE HIM ALONE! YOU MEN – PUT SOME AMMO ON BOARD MY TANK !
YOU HEARD THE MAJOR! START LOADING !
AIEE ! BUT THESE COPS ARE BUTCHERS!
DANKE, HERR MAJOR! WE WERE JUST CARRYING OUT THE ORDERS OF HERR GAULIETER KASTNER – THE AREA CONTROLLER!
KASTNER !
KASTNER, AN ARDENT NAZI LEADER, HAD CLASHED MANY TIMES WITH HELLMAN EARLIER IN THE WAR.
SO, THAT SS BUTCHER, KASTNER, WHO HATES MY GUTS, IS STILL ALIVE! BUT RIGHT NOW WE'VE MORE IMMEDIATE PROBLEMS! ARM YOURSELVES – WE'RE GOING TO MAKE ANOTHER ATTACK ON THE SOVIETS !
YOU HEARD THE MAJOR ! MOVE !
SOON --
SO NOW IT'S THE RUSSIANS WE TAKE ON AGAIN ? IT'S GETTING TO BE SO WE DON'T KNOW WHICH WAY TO TURN !
JA, WE'LL MAKE ANOTHER STAND HERE – BUT I HOPE I CATCH SIGHT OF KASTNER BEFORE BERLIN FALLS ! WE HAVE AN OLD SCORE TO SETTLE!
BUT ONE OF HELLMAN'S CREW WAS WORKING AGAINST HIM – HEILER!
YOU WORK FOR GERMANY, MAJOR – NOT HITLER! IF I GET THE CHANCE – I MUST MAKE SURE GAULIETER KASTNER CATCHES YOU FIRST!
ARE HELLMAN'S DAYS NUMBERED ? SEE NEXT WEEK !

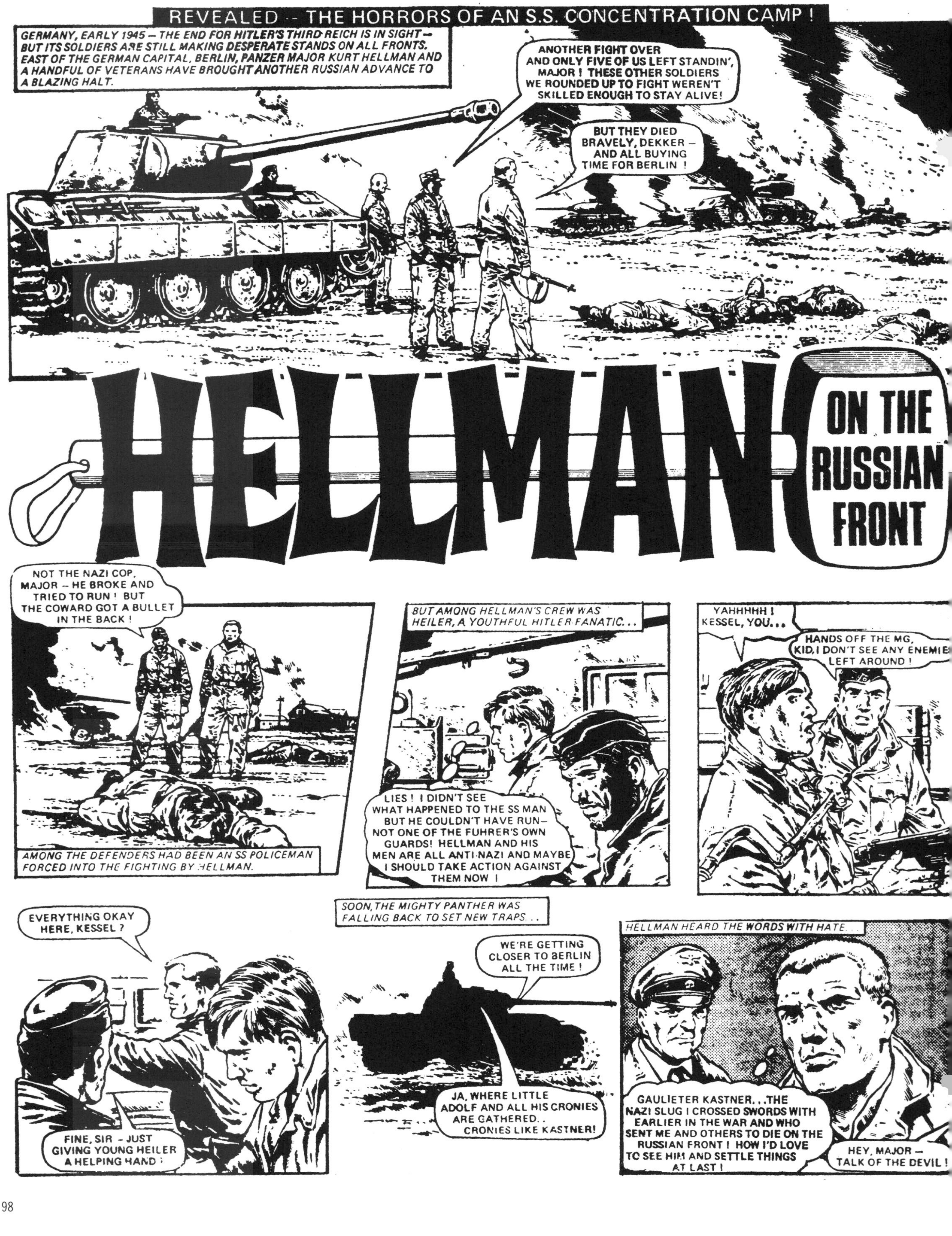

REVEALED – THE HORRORS OF AN S.S. CONCENTRATION CAMP !

GERMANY, EARLY 1945 – THE END FOR HITLER'S THIRD REICH IS IN SIGHT – BUT ITS SOLDIERS ARE STILL MAKING DESPERATE STANDS ON ALL FRONTS. EAST OF THE GERMAN CAPITAL, BERLIN, PANZER MAJOR KURT HELLMAN AND A HANDFUL OF VETERANS HAVE BROUGHT ANOTHER RUSSIAN ADVANCE TO A BLAZING HALT.

ANOTHER FIGHT OVER AND ONLY FIVE OF US LEFT STANDIN', MAJOR ! THESE OTHER SOLDIERS WE ROUNDED UP TO FIGHT WEREN'T SKILLED ENOUGH TO STAY ALIVE!

BUT THEY DIED BRAVELY, DEKKER – AND ALL BUYING TIME FOR BERLIN !

HELLMAN ON THE RUSSIAN FRONT

NOT THE NAZI COP, MAJOR – HE BROKE AND TRIED TO RUN ! BUT THE COWARD GOT A BULLET IN THE BACK !
AMONG THE DEFENDERS HAD BEEN AN SS POLICEMAN FORCED INTO THE FIGHTING BY HELLMAN.

BUT AMONG HELLMAN'S CREW WAS HEILER, A YOUTHFUL HITLER FANATIC...
LIES ! I DIDN'T SEE WHAT HAPPENED TO THE SS MAN BUT HE COULDN'T HAVE RUN – NOT ONE OF THE FUHRER'S OWN GUARDS! HELLMAN AND HIS MEN ARE ALL ANTI-NAZI AND MAYBE I SHOULD TAKE ACTION AGAINST THEM NOW !

YAHHHHH ! KESSEL, YOU...
HANDS OFF THE MG, KID, I DON'T SEE ANY ENEMIES LEFT AROUND !

EVERYTHING OKAY HERE, KESSEL ?
FINE, SIR – JUST GIVING YOUNG HEILER A HELPING HAND !

SOON, THE MIGHTY PANTHER WAS FALLING BACK TO SET NEW TRAPS...
WE'RE GETTING CLOSER TO BERLIN ALL THE TIME !
JA, WHERE LITTLE ADOLF AND ALL HIS CRONIES ARE GATHERED.. CRONIES LIKE KASTNER!

HELLMAN HEARD THE WORDS WITH HATE...
GAULIETER KASTNER... THE NAZI SLUG I CROSSED SWORDS WITH EARLIER IN THE WAR AND WHO SENT ME AND OTHERS TO DIE ON THE RUSSIAN FRONT ! HOW I'D LOVE TO SEE HIM AND SETTLE THINGS AT LAST !
HEY, MAJOR – TALK OF THE DEVIL !

AT THE ROADSIDE BY A FOREST TRACK WAS A LARGE SIGNPOST –
THAT'S KASTNER'S NAME ON THAT SIGN . . . SAYING NO ENTRY TO AN SS CAMP UP THERE IN THE WOODS!
SS CAMP? I WONDER WHAT SOUGHT OF CAMP THAT IS ?
MAX DROVE FOR THE POST
HAW, SORRY, MAJOR! BUT EVERY TIME I SEE A SWASTIKA THESE DAYS, I WANNA STEAM ROLL OVER IT !
FORGET ABOUT THE CAMP AND LET'S KEEP TO THE ROAD !
BUT
AN SS CAMP FULL OF THE FUHRER'S LOYAL GUARDS! NOW'S MY CHANCE . I WILL TELL THEM ABOUT HELLMAN AND HIS THUGS !
WHAT THE ? HEILER! THE LITTLE FOOL'S OPENED HIS HATCH AND DIVED OUT !
HEILER – HALT ! THAT'S AN ORDER !
GO TO HELL, MAJOR – I DON'T OBEY TRAITOR SCUM ! THE SS WILL SETTLE WITH YOU !
OKAY, MAX – SWING ON TO THAT FOREST TRACK AND WE'LL CUT THE LITTLE FOOL OFF BEFORE HE REACHES HIS NAZI FRIENDS AT THE CAMP !
HELLMAN AND HIS THUGS ARE COMING AFTER ME! MUST. . .MUST – REACH THE SS CAMP !
JA, THERE IT IS BELOW AND I SEE BLACK HELMETS AND UNIFORMS! HEY – MEN OF THE FUHRER'S SS !
ACHTUNG ! UP THERE !
BELOW –
MEIN GOTT – IS HE RUSSIAN ? THE FRONT CAN'T BE HERE YET !
NEIN, HE'S GERMAN! A STRAGGLER-SOLDIER! SHUT HIM UP, WATCHTOWER !
JAWOHL!

NEIN! NEIN! I'M A FRIEND! I'M LOYAL TO THE FUHRER-AIEEEEE!
WE GOT HIM, HERR KOMMANDANT!
GUT – NOW START THE WORK! FIRST THE MACHINE-GUNS THEN WE'LL DESTROY THE CORPSES! THERE'LL BE NO EVIDENCE LEFT TO SHOW WHAT'S HAPPENED AT SS CAMP 35!
BUT HELLMAN AND BIG MAX HAD REACHED THE FAR SIDE OF THE RIDGE...
GOTT – THEY OPENED FIRE ON THE KID! WHAT'S GOIN' ON IN THAT CAMP DOWN THERE?
LET'S TAKE A CLOSER LOOK AND SEE!
BOTH MEN LOOKED DOWN IN SHOCK...
GOTT – IT'S A PRISON CAMP OF SOME SORT AND THOSE SS SCUM ARE MURDERING ALL THE INMATES!
EXTERMINATING THEM LIKE BUGS!
AN EXTERMINATION CAMP... SO THEY EXIST! ALL THROUGH THE WAR WE HEARD RUMOURS BUT RECKONED IT WAS JUST ENEMY PROPAGANDA!
JA, IT'S TRUE!
AND SO WE'VE BEEN HELPING BUY TIME FOR BUTCHERY LIKE THIS! I THOUGHT THE SS WERE THE SORT OF RUNNING SORES EVERY ARMY OF EVERY COUNTRY HAS! BUT THIS – THIS IS A PURELY GERMAN DISEASE!
HELLMAN AND HIS CREW LEAPT FOR THEIR FIGHTING SEATS...
SO, COME ON... WE'VE NO AMMO LEFT... JUST THE TANK TO TAKE US INSIDE THAT CAMP AND CLEAN THOSE SS SLIME OUT!
WE'RE WITH YOU, MAJOR!
GERMAN AGAINST GERMAN...WHO WILL WIN? ORDER YOUR NEXT COPY NOW!

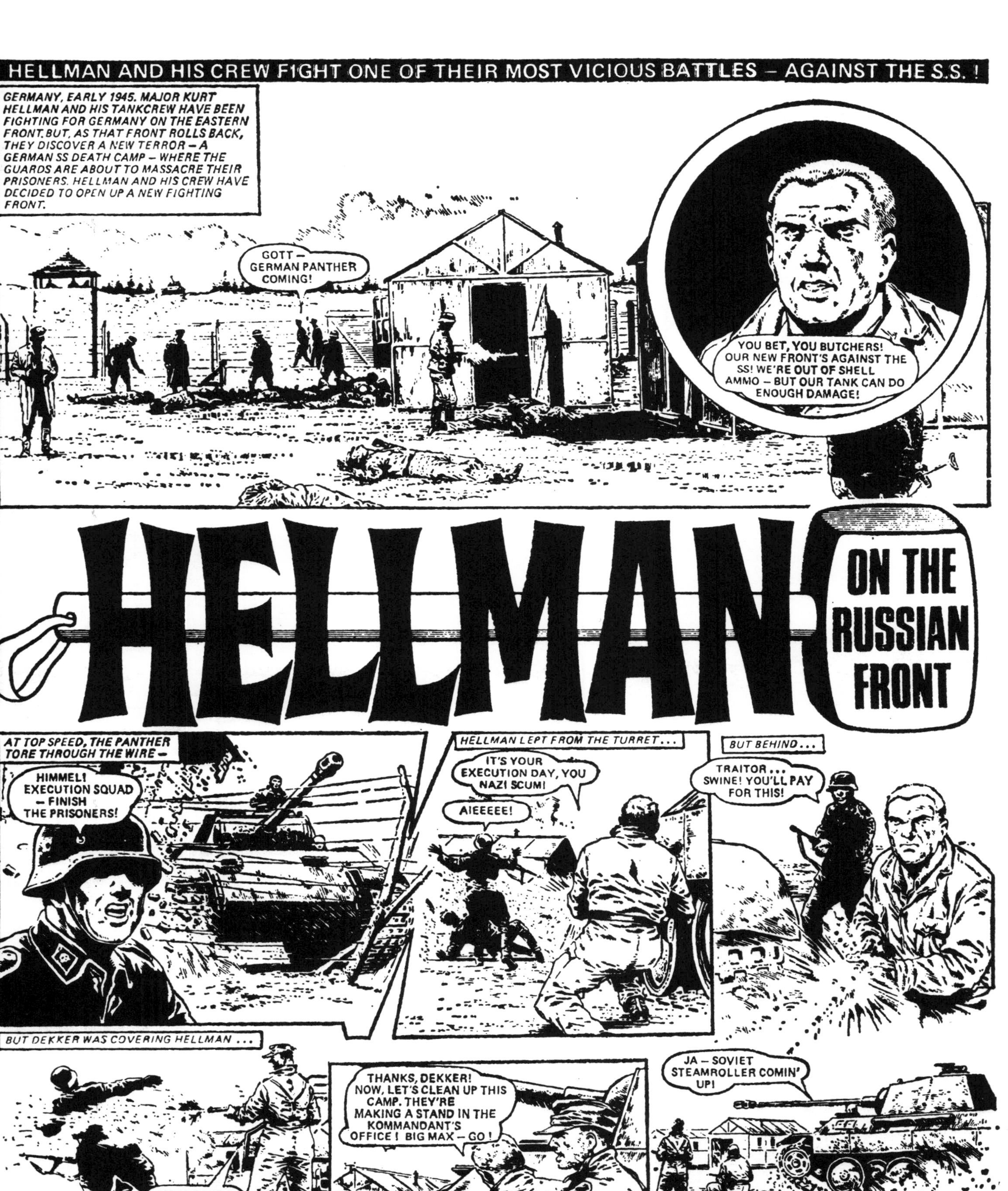
HELLMAN AND HIS CREW FIGHT ONE OF THEIR MOST VICIOUS BATTLES – AGAINST THE S.S. !
GERMANY, EARLY 1945. MAJOR KURT HELLMAN AND HIS TANKCREW HAVE BEEN FIGHTING FOR GERMANY ON THE EASTERN FRONT. BUT, AS THAT FRONT ROLLS BACK, THEY DISCOVER A NEW TERROR – A GERMAN SS DEATH CAMP – WHERE THE GUARDS ARE ABOUT TO MASSACRE THEIR PRISONERS. HELLMAN AND HIS CREW HAVE DECIDED TO OPEN UP A NEW FIGHTING FRONT.
GOTT – GERMAN PANTHER COMING!
YOU BET, YOU BUTCHERS! OUR NEW FRONT'S AGAINST THE SS! WE'RE OUT OF SHELL AMMO – BUT OUR TANK CAN DO ENOUGH DAMAGE!
HELLMAN
ON THE RUSSIAN FRONT
AT TOP SPEED, THE PANTHER TORE THROUGH THE WIRE –
HIMMEL! EXECUTION SQUAD – FINISH THE PRISONERS!
HELLMAN LEPT FROM THE TURRET...
IT'S YOUR EXECUTION DAY, YOU NAZI SCUM!
AIEEEEE!
BUT BEHIND...
TRAITOR... SWINE! YOU'LL PAY FOR THIS!
BUT DEKKER WAS COVERING HELLMAN...
WRONG MOVE, MURDERER! IT'S NO CONTEST WHEN YOU COME UP AGAINST MEN WHO CAN FIGHT BACK!
THANKS, DEKKER! NOW, LET'S CLEAN UP THIS CAMP. THEY'RE MAKING A STAND IN THE KOMMANDANT'S OFFICE! BIG MAX – GO!
JA – SOVIET STEAMROLLER COMIN' UP!

HILFE – HILFE – SS HQ, SCHNELL, SCHNELL!
SCREAM IN HELL – COURTESY OF MAJOR HELLMAN AND CREW!
NEIN – AIEEEEEEEEE!

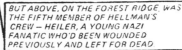

BUT ABOVE, ON THE FOREST RIDGE, WAS THE FIFTH MEMBER OF HELLMAN'S CREW – HEILER, A YOUNG NAZI FANATIC WHO'D BEEN WOUNDED PREVIOUSLY AND LEFT FOR DEAD
GOTT – HELLMAN AND HIS THUGS HAVE WIPED OUT THE ENTIRE SS GUARD!

LOOK AT THOSE POOR SAPS STARIN' AT US. STILL SCARED!
THEY'RE TERRIFIED OF ANYONE IN UNIFORM! THEIR MINDS HAVE GONE! THE DAMNED SS HAVE A LOT TO ANSWER FOR!
HEY, MAJOR!

LOOK, SIR – ON THIS SS MAP! DEATH CAMPS DOTTED ALL THE WAY BACK TO BERLIN!
AND AT EACH ONE THEY'LL BE PLANNING FAST MASSACRES AS THE RUSSIANS GET CLOSER!
UNLESS WE MOVE FASTER! MOUNT UP!

YOU PRISONERS – GET OUT OF HERE! YOU'RE FREE – MOVE!
NOBODY'LL EVER BELIEVE WHO BAILED THEM OUT!

HEY – HEILER, SIR! WE LEFT HIS BODY THERE BUT IT'S GONE! HE MUST STILL BE ALIVE!
WHO CARES? GOOD RIDDANCE – TO A ROTTEN APPLE, I SAY!

BUT HEILER HAD CRAWLED INTO THE DESERTED CONCENTRATION CAMP –
NOBODY SAW ME! THE KOMMANDANT'S PHONE IS STILL WORKING. NOW I'LL TRY AND FIX THOSE TRAITORS!

AND HERE IS A LIST OF SS NUMBERS – INCLUDING THE BERLIN OFFICE OF GAULIETER KASTNER – A NAME I HEARD HELLMAN MENTION BEFORE! I'LL PHONE HIM!
KASTNER, A NAZI OFFICER, HAD CLASHED WITH HELLMAN EARLIER IN THE WAR!

MILES AWAY IN BERLIN.
HERR KASTNER, A STRANGE CALL FROM THE FRONT! SOMEONE WHO SAYS HE'S A FRIEND . . . WANTS TO WARN YOU OF A MAN NAMED HELLMAN!
HELLMAN? GIVE ME THAT!

HERR KASTNER, SIR – WE'VE NEVER MET, BUT WE'VE MADE MUTUAL ACQUAINTANCE OF HELLMAN. I KNOW HE HATES YOU, SIR, AND HE'S HEADING YOUR WAY LIKE A MAD DOG – WIPING OUT SS CAMPS! YOU MUST DO SOMETHING!
I – I WILL, MY YOUNG FRIEND! TRY AND FOLLOW THEM FOR ME WHILE I ARRANGE SOMETHING MYSELF!

MILLIONS OF RUSSIANS ARE HEADING THIS WAY — YET YOU ARE WORRIED ABOUT ONE OFFICER -- A GERMAN?
YOU DON'T KNOW HELLMAN! HE'S MORE DANGEROUS TO ME THAN ANY RUSSIAN! GET ME THE SS BARRACKS!
FOLLOWING THE RAILWAY, HELLMAN'S PANTHER APPROACHED ITS NEXT OBJECTIVE.
THIS LINE LEADS US WEST TOWARDS BERLIN!
THAT BRANCH LINE, MAJOR — THE SS BOARD MEANS THERE IS ANOTHER DEATH CAMP AT THE END OF THE LINE!
FIVE MILES FURTHER ON . . .
AND THERE IT IS, MAJOR . . . THE CAMP! AND LOOK . . !
STRIPED PYJAMA SUITS — THE PRISONERS ARE STILL ALIVE!
YEAH, NO SIGN OF THE GUARDS!
HEY, HEY — HELP US, PLEASE! OUR GUARDS HAVE RUN!
HEAR THAT? THE SS HAVE GONE! PITY — ALL WE CAN DO IS SMASH THEIR GATE DOWN FOR THEM!
BUT I SENSE SOMETHING IS WRONG HERE!
NEXT SECOND
THERE YOU ARE, BOYS — YOU'RE FREE TO GO!
HEY— THEY'RE MOBBING US!
SUDDENLY
OKAY, NOW!
HECK, UNDER THEIR PYJAMA SUITS . . . BLACK UNIFORMS!
THEY'RE SS — A TRICK! A DIRTY TRAP!
HELLMAN CURSED . . .
IT'S NO USE, MEN — WE'VE BEEN TRICKED!
JA, GAULIETER KASTNER WILL BE DELIGHTED TO KNOW YOU'VE BEEN CAUGHT! WHO'S THIS COMING?
ME — HEILER, HERR SCHARFUHRER! I WAS THE ONE WHO GAVE YOU THE WARNING!
SOON . . .
THE KID — ONE OF OUR OWN CREW FOULED US UP!
NOW THEY'RE GOING TO HANG US! STAND TO ATTENTION, YOU THREE — LOOKS LIKE WE'VE FACED THE FRONT TOGETHER FOR THE LAST TIME! WE'RE GOING TO DIE DIRTY BUT AT LEAST WE FEEL A BIT CLEANER INSIDE!

DEATH AT THE HANDS OF HIS COUNTRYMEN ! IS THIS THE END FOR HELLMAN ?

THE HANGMAN'S NOOSE AWAITS MAJOR HELLMAN AND HIS CREW!
EARLY 1945. GERMANY, SURROUNDED AND SLOWLY BEING ROLLED BACK LIKE A CARPET, HAS REVEALED ITS DIRTY SWEEPINGS WHICH SHOCK EVEN GERMAN SOLDIERS . . . SS DEATH CAMPS! MAJOR KURT HELLMAN AND HIS TOUGH TANK CREW HAVE PREVENTED A MASSACRE OF CONCENTRATION CAMP PRISONERS – BUT ARE NOW THEMSELVES CAPTIVES OF THE SS . . .
HELLMAN, YOU AND YOUR THREE MEN WILL BE HUNG AS TRAITORS TO ADOLF HITLER'S REICH! YOU SHOULD HAVE STUCK TO FIGHTING BATTLES AND KEPT YOUR NOSE OUT OF SS BUSINESS!
AND LEAVE YOU THUGS TO CARRY OUT MORE BUTCHERY?
HELLMAN AND HIS CREW HAD BEEN CAUGHT IN AN SS TRAP AFTER BEING BETRAYED BY THEIR FIFTH CREWMAN – THE YOUNG GUN-LOADER NAMED HEILER . . .
YOU AND YOUR SCUM ARE NO SAINTS, HELLMAN! YOU DARED STAND AGAINST THE FUHRER!
BIG MAX AND DEKKER, THE TWO EX-CONVICTS OF HELLMAN'S CREW, SPRANG FORWARD . . .
THE LITTLE PUNK PUT OUR NECKS IN A NOOSE! LET'S GET HIM!
JA, COME ON!
STOP THEM! STOP THEM!
WITH THEIR HANDS TIED, NEITHER GOT MORE THAN A FEW YARDS . . .
YOU . . . AHHHH!
YOU DID THAT DELIBERATELY TO GET A QUICK BULLET – BUT YOU WILL NOT BE SO LUCKY! YOU'RE GOING TO DANGLE SLOWLY AND DIE IN AGONY AT THE END OF A ROPE!
HELLMAN
ON THE RUSSIAN FRONT
THE CRIPPLED SERGEANT KESSEL WAS THE LAST SURVIVING MEMBER OF HELLMAN'S ORIGINAL CREW . . .
THOSE JAILBIRDS WERE MAD TO THINK THAT WOULD DO ANY GOOD!
WRONG, KESSEL – I THINK THEY GOT JUST WHAT THEY WANTED!
A FLASH OF STEEL – A KNIFE! THOSE TWO CONS MUST'VE LIFTED IT WHEN THEY FELL AGAINST THAT SS GOON!
BUT, MOMENTS LATER, THE ROPES WERE ROUND THEIR NECKS . . .
HEILER, EACH MAN HERE SAVED YOUR LIFE ON THE RUSSIAN FRONT! WE DON'T EXPECT THANKS – JUST GET THE HELL OUT OF HERE BEFORE THE HANGING BEGINS! GO FOR A WALK ROUND YOUR SS FRIENDS' CAMP!
YEAH, GO ON, PUNK – SCRAM!
C'MON, DEKKER – HURRY! USE THAT BLADE!
IT . . . IT'S NO USE, MAX! CAN'T . . . CAN'T SAW THROUGH THIS SS LEATHER!
IT'S NO GOOD, SIR! EVEN THE JAILBIRDS CAN'T GET US OUT OF THIS MESS!
WAIT – OVER THERE BY THE BLOCKHOUSE!
HEILER EMERGED FROM THE STONE BUILDING WHITE-FACED . . .
OUR YOUNG FANATIC HAS JUST SEEN THE MASSACRED REMAINS OF THIS CAMP'S INMATES! NOW HE KNOWS WHAT HIS FUHRER'S GLORIOUS SS HAVE REALLY BEEN DOING!

THE SS SCHARFUHRER GRINNED UP AT HELLMAN...
HELLMAN - YOU HAVE ONLY A FEW MOMENTS TO LIVE. ONE OF MY MEN IS FETCHING A CAMERA - TO RECORD YOUR DEATH FOR GAULIETER KASTNER IN BERLIN! IT IS A MOMENT HE HAS LONG AWAITED!
ONLY SECONDS LEFT BUT WAIT - WHAT IS HEILER DOING BEHIND THAT RAILWAY CAR?
HEILER, UNSEEN BY THE GUARDS CREPT TO TO THE TANK ...
WHAT'S HE UP TO, MAJOR? WHAT'S HE LUGGIN'?
AND...
THAT NOISE! IT'S MACHINERY WHIRRING SOMEWHERE!
HERR SCHARFUHRER - SOMEONE'S INSIDE THE TANK!
ALL THIS TIME I'VE BELIEVED IN THE FUHRER AND THE REICH! BUT NOT AFTER WHAT I'VE JUST SEEN...
THE POWERFUL 75 GUN SPOKE ...
... BECAUSE NOW I KNOW THE SS FOR WHAT THEY REALLY ARE... MURDERERS!
AIEEEEE!
JUST THEN
SIR, DEKKER'S CUT HIMSELF FREE!
YEAH - BUT UNLESS THE KID GETS THE PORT MG GOING FAST - IT WON'T MATTER A DAMN!
THAT INSTANT, THE TANK'S MG BARKED INTO LIFE... SPRAYING DEATH INTO THE SS RANKS!
THE PUNK KID DID IT! HE MUST'VE READ MY MIND!
WHEN ALL WAS QUIET AGAIN...
WELL, HEILER?
I... I'VE BEEN A FOOL, MAJOR. THOSE PRISONERS IN THAT BLOCKHOUSE... IT WAS TERRIBLE! CAN YOU FORGIVE ME AND LET ME JOIN YOUR CREW AGAIN?
OKAY, HEILER, THE PAST IS FORGOTTEN! WE'RE BACK TOGETHER AS A BATTLE TEAM!
LOOK, SIR - ALONG THE RAILWAY LINE! A TRAIN COMING!

RED FLAG ON THE FRONT! A RUSSIAN WAR TRAIN HEADING STRAIGHT FOR BERLIN WITH RAILGUNS READY TO BLAST THE CITY TO BITS!
UNLESS WE BRING IT TO AN UNSCHEDULED HALT! GET MORE AMMO FROM THAT RAILCAR... FAST!
ACHTUNG!
COME ON KID!
THIS IS WHERE THE RUSSIAN ADVANCE GOES OFF THE RAILS! FEUR!
AND NEXT SECOND...
NIET — AIEEEEEEEEEEEE!
THAT'S ONE LOAD OF RUSSKIES THAT WON'T BE JOINING IN THE KILL AT BERLIN — BUT THERE'S PLENTY MORE COMING ALONG BEHIND THEM! WE'VE GOT TO MAKE IT TO BERLIN... IN TIME FOR THE LAST BATTLE!
DON'T MISS NEXT WEEK'S EXCITING ISSUE! PLACE YOUR ORDER NOW!

HELLMAN FIGHTS DESPERATELY FOR BERLIN !

APRIL, 1945 – THE LAST ACT IS ABOUT TO TAKE PLACE ON THE RUSSIAN FRONT. . . THE BATTLE FOR BERLIN. KNOWING THEIR CAPITAL IS SURROUNDED, THE GERMAN DEFENDERS PREPARE FOR A LAST FIGHT. AMONG THEM, THE FIVE VETERANS WHO SLIPPED IN JUST BEFORE THE RING SNAPPED SHUT. . . PANZER MAJOR KURT HELLMAN AND HIS TANK CREW –
LÜBECK
ROSTOCK
HAMBURG
BERLIN
DESSAU
LEIPZIG
DRESDEN
CHEMITZ
ZWICKAU

BERLIN AT LAST! BUT THE CAPITAL OF THE REICH'S JUST ONE BIG RAT-TRAP! THERE ARE BOTH DECENT FOLK AND DIRTY KILLERS SHELTERING HERE – AND WE'LL HAVE TO DEFEND THEM ALL!

I JUST HOPE I GET TO MEET ONE OF THE RATS SOONER OR LATER. GAULIETER KASTNER, THE NAZI DISTRICT LEADER, HOLED UP WITH THE REST OF HITLER'S GANG!
KASTNER HAD BEEN RESPONSIBLE FOR THE MURDER OF MANY OF HELLMAN'S COMRADES BEHIND THE LINES IN PREVIOUS ACTIONS –

HELLMAN ON THE RUSSIAN FRONT

IN THE CITY CENTRE, ROUND THE CHANCELLERY, KASTNER WAS AMONG NAZI LEADERS GROUPED ROUND THEIR FUHRER –
THIS IS THE OBSERVATORY WHERE THE FUHRER WATCHES THE STARS FOR SIGNS OF FINAL VICTORY. HE RESTS IN THE BUNKER RIGHT NOW.
BUT THE TELESCOPE IS POINTED TO EARTH, HERR BORMANN!

JA, KASTNER, BECAUSE SOME OF US HAVE OUR EYES ON CLOSER THINGS. . . THE RUSSIAN FRONT!

MEIN GOTT, ROCKET ATTACK ON THE SOUTH-EAST SUBURBS!

IN THE SUBURBS, HELLMAN'S TANK WAS RACING TO FIND SHELTER –

STALIN ORGANS COMING AT US AGAIN! THEY'RE GIVING US ALL THE FIRE POWER THEY'VE GOT! WE'VE GOT TO GET UNDER COVER SOMEWHERE!

THE CITY ZOO. . . A MASS OF CAGES AND ANIMAL HOUSES! THAT WON'T BE ON THE RUSSIAN'S TARGET LIST!

BETTER HURRY, SIR! THOSE STALIN ORGANS ARE HITTIN' THE HIGH NOTE BEFORE THEY SIGN OFF!

THE PANZER V RACED INTO THE ZOO GROUNDS –

JA, THEN IT'LL BE THE TURN OF THEIR SHOCK ARMIES! MOVE ON, MAX!

AS THEY REACHED A LONG LINE OF CAGES, THERE CAME SUDDEN SILENCE FROM THE NEARBY STREETS –

ROCKETING'S STOPPED, SIR – THEY'LL BE COMIN' NOW! WHERE DO WE HIDE?

RIGHT HERE! GET OUT YOUR SPANNERS. . . OUR PANTHER HAS FOUND A HIDE!

IN USUAL RED ARMY FASHION, GROUND FORCES RACED FORWARD THE INSTANT THE ROCKETING CEASED –
ONWARD, MY SIBERIAN ANIMALS! BUTCHER ANYTHING THAT MOVES IN THE BERLIN STREETS!
NIETCHEVO. . .NOTHING STIRRING! WAIT – SOUNDS OVER THERE!
A ZOO! OUR SIBERIANS HAVE THE SMELL OF FOOD!
THEY RACED THROUGH THE ZOO GAT
HA – THEY'RE SHOOTING THE ANIMALS FOR FOOD – I FORGOT MY MEN ARE ALWAYS HUNGRY AND THEY LOVE RAW MEAT!
BY KILLING EVERYTHING IN THE ZOO, THEY'RE SAVING US ANY FOOD SUPPLY PROBLEMS! LET'S TAKE A LOOK AT THE BEASTS IN THOSE CAGES BEFORE THEY'RE SLAUGHTERED! AH, THE BIG CATS!
DA, INTERESTING. . . ALMOST AS GOOD AS THE MOSCOW STATE ZOO! LIONS, CHEETAHS, PUMAS. . .
AND LAST, BUT NOT LEAST. . .THE PANTHER!
KZANI-GERMAN TANK! NIET!
DEKKER, HELLMAN'S TANK GUNNER, COULD NOT MISS –
AIEEEEEEEEEE!
OKAY, MAX-FORWARD! THEY'VE HEARD OUR ROAR!
LET'S LET THIS ANIMAL OUT OF IT'S CAGE!
AIEEEEE!

KESSEL'S FAST FIRING 75 GUN SPOKE AGAIN AND AGAIN –
GOT ALL THEIR WHEELS – BUT THOSE SIBERIANS ARE SWARMING EVERYWHERE! LET'S GET OUT FAST!
HITTIN' REVERSE NOW!

MAX – YOU BACKED US IN THROUGH THE REPTILE HOUSE!
REPTILHAUS
JA, WHAT'S THE BETS THOSE SLANTEYES CAN'T READ?

THE SWARMS OF SIBERIANS RACED AFTER THE TANK AS IT REVERSED CRAZILY THROUGH THE BUILDING –
YEAH, HERE THEY COME – THEY CAN'T READ!

AHEEEE ! SNAKES EVERYWHERE !
OKAY, MAX, WE'VE HAD OUR DAY AT THE ZOO! LET'S GO SOMEPLACE ELSE!

WITHIN MINUTES, THE PANTHER WAS ROARING THROUGH THE RUINED STREETS OF BERLIN ONCE MORE –
NOW THERE'S JUST ONE OTHER LITTLE SNAKE I'D LIKE TO SEE BEFORE THE BATTLE OF BERLIN IS OVER..!
GAULIETER KASTNER ?

JA, KASTNER! WE'RE BEING SLOWLY PUSHED FURTHER INTO THE CITY CENTRE WHERE THE WHOLE NEST OF VENOMOUS NAZIS ARE! MAYBE THEN I'LL MEET HIM FACE-TO-FACE AT LAST!
BUT
HELLMAN...IT'S HIM! HE'S STILL ALIVE AND KICKING... AND IN BERLIN!

GAULIETER KASTNER WATCHED IN SHOCK TEN MILES AWAY –
I'VE SEEN YOU FIRST THROUGH THE FUHRER'S ASTRONOMER'S TELE-SCOPE! I DON'T NEED TO LOOK TO THE STARS TO TELL YOUR FUTURE I'M GOING TO MAKE SURE YOU'RE KILLED BEFORE YOU GET ANY CLOSER TO ME!

WHAT HAS KASTNER GOT PLANNED FOR HELLMAN ? MORE NEXT ISSUE !

KASTNER GIVES THE ORDER... HELLMAN MUST DIE!
APRIL, 1945 — THE FINAL BATTLE OF THE RUSSIAN FRONT RAGES — THE BATTLE FOR BERLIN ITSELF. WITH THEIR MASSIVE SUPERIORITY, THE RUSSIANS KNOW VICTORY WILL BE THEIRS.. BUT DIEHARD VETERANS, LIKE MAJOR KURT HELLMAN, ARE MAKING THEM SUFFER LOSSES FOR EVERY STREET —
U Bahn
WE'RE BEING SQUEEZED BACK INTO THE CITY CENTRE... HARDLY ANY STREETS LEFT BETWEEN US AND HITLER AND HIS GANG OF NAZIS, BUT I'M ALSO GETTING CLOSER TO KASTNER!
THROUGHOUT THE RUSSIAN FRONT CAMPAIGN, HELLMAN AND A PROMINENT NAZI HAD CARRIED ON A RUNNING FEUD. HELLMAN KNEW THEY WERE BOTH TRAPPED IN BERLIN —
HELLMAN
ON THE RUSSIAN FRONT
BUT IN THE OBSERVATORY BUILT ONTO THE CHANCELLERY COMPLEX, GAULIETER KASTNER HAD A GIANT TELESCOPE TRAINED ON HELLMAN IN THE STREETS BEYOND —
I SEE YOU, HELLMAN -- BUT SURELY YOU MUST BE STOPPED IN THE STREETS WITH RUSSIAN ARMOUR ALL AROUND! YOU'VE GOT TO DIE! GOT TO!
POSITIONED ROUND THE CHANCELLERY WAS DEFENCE ARTILLERY —
HEY, BELOW — I'VE SEEN A GOOD TARGET FOR YOU! MASSIVE RUSSIAN ARMOUR IN THE UNTER-DEN-LINDEN!
JAWOHL, HERR GAULIETER — WE'LL SMASH THEM!
MOMENTS LATER —
GOTT— GUNFIRE LANDING BEHIND! THEY'RE OUR OWN GUNS FROM THE CITY CENTRE!
THERE'S A WALL OF GUNFIRE BEHIND — AND THE RUSSIANS ARE COMING FOR OUR THROATS! WHERE DO WE GO, SIR?
LOOK, OVER THERE! LET'S TRY UNDERGROUND!
U Bahn

HELLMAN TURNED—
LET'S SEE IF YOU CAN GET THIS BEAST DOWN THOSE SUBWAY STEPS, MAX!
AS THE YOUTHFUL HEILER, WHO HAD PREVIOUSLY BEEN A HITLER YOUTH FANATIC, DIRECTED THE TANK. . .
YAHHHHH!
WATCH OUT, HEILER, YOU ALMOST HAD YOUR HEAD OFF THERE! NO NEED TO PROVE ANYTHING TO US ANY MORE!
THOSE ESCALATORS — CAN WE GET DOWN THERE?
THIS CAT CAN GO ANYWHERE, SIR! JUST WATCH!
HELLMAN SMILED-
JA. . . NOW WE'LL MAKE OUR WAY THROUGH THE STREETS UNDERGROUND — AND COME UP AT THE NEXT STATION FOR THE NEXT ROUND!
STRANGE HOW THAT 88 FIRE WAS ALMOST ZEROED ON US, SIR!
KASTNER HAD HIS 'SCOPE TRAINED ON THE STATION —
GOTT — THEY'VE GOT INTO THE UNDER-GROUND ITSELF! HELLMAN'S STILL KICKING AND I'VE GOT TO MAKE SURE HE'S KILLED!
KASTNER LOOKED DOWN INTO THE CHANCELLERY GARDEN —
A KNIGHT'S CROSS PARADE. . . THE FUHRER'S STILL HOLDING CEREMONIES IN HIS BUNKER! WAIT, THAT TALL ONE — I'VE SEEN HIS PICTURE IN NEWSREELS!
JA. . . THE MAN CALLED 'VIKING' — THE TOP SCORING SNIPER OF THE WAFFEN SS, AND HE'LL BE A LOYAL NAZI! JA — HE CAN BE THE ONE TO HELP!
A PRIVILEGE TO MEET YOU, GAULIETER KASTNER. MY NAME IS VIKING — FROM THE SS VIKING REGIMENT. THREE HUNDRED KILLS ON THE RUSSIAN FRONT — ALL IMPORTANT TARGETS, BUT NOW I'M WASTED HERE!
I HAVE ONE IMPORTANT KILL FOR YOU — THOUGH HE'S NOT RUSSIAN! LISTEN CLOSELY. . .
BELOW, IN A WIDE U-BAHN TUNNEL —
TOLD YOU THE PANTHER COULD GO ANY-WHERE, SIR! LUCKY ALL THE ELECTRIC POWER'S CUT IN BERLIN!
JA — NOW WE'RE UNDER THE NEXT STREET!
OKAY, WE'RE AT THE STATION — BUT THE STAIRS TO THE STREETS ARE BLOCKED WITH RUBBLE!
TELL THOSE REFUGEES TO STAND ASIDE! I'LL GIVE US A STAIRCASE — WITH A SEVENTY-FIVE!

BUT ABOVE, AS THE SMOKE CLEARED FROM THE UNDERGROUND EXPLOSION –
HMM – THIS HELLMAN MUST BE SOMEONE... TAKING A TANK INTO THE UNDERGROUND! BUT IF HE IS ANTI-NAZI, THEN HE DESERVES TO DIE!
BUT–
HMM – THE RUSSIAN FRONT'S ALSO ARRIVED! RED SHOCK INFANTRY – AND THEY'RE GOING IN TO CHECK OUT THE SUBWAY. I'LL WAIT AND SEE WHAT HAPPENS!
DAVAI... DAVAI!
BELOW –
WAIT – SOMETHING ABOVE!
HEILER YELLED –
AIEEEEEEEEEEEE!
I'LL GET THEM, SIR!
GOOD WORK, BOY – BUT YOUR CLOTHES ARE CUT TO RIBBONS! HERE, TAKE MY PANZER JACKET!
THANKS, SIR! I'VE GOT RID OF MY HITLER-YOUTH RAGS AT LAST!
ABOVE –
JACKET WITH MAJOR'S BARS! THIS MUST BE HELLMAN!
THE CRACK OF THE SNIPER'S BULLET ECHOED IN THE STREETS –
HEILER!
HE – HE'S DEAD! POOR KID DIDN'T KNOW WHAT HIT HIM! THE DIRTY RUSSIAN SCUM!
THAT RIFLE SHOT WASN'T RUSSIAN!
IT SOUNDED LIKE A MANNLICHER... A GERMAN RIFLE! COULD IT BE KASTNER'S ONTO US? INTO THE TANK AND WE'LL GO OUT SHIELDED!
THE TANK IS COMING OUT WITH ALL HATCHES CLOSED FROM ANOTHER BULLET! IT COULDN'T HAVE BEEN HELLMAN I SHOT! I MUST FOLLOW UNTIL HE SHOWS HIMSELF AGAIN! THEN, BEFORE BERLIN FALLS, HELLMAN WILL DIE!
IS HELLMAN DESTINED TO DIE BY A GERMAN BULLET? FIND OUT NEXT WEEK!

GERMANY'S MOST DEADLY SNIPER HAS A BULLET WITH HELLMAN'S NAME ON IT!
HELLMAN
ON THE RUSSIAN FRONT
APRIL, 1945. THE BATTLE OF BERLIN RAGES WITH THE RUSSIANS CLOSING IN THROUGH THE CITY ON ALL SIDES. BUT THEY SUFFER EVEN LARGER STREET-FIGHTING LOSSES THAN STALINGRAD AT THE HANDS OF DIEHARD VETERANS LIKE MAJOR KURT HELLMAN AND HIS TANK CREW...
WE'LL USE THIS CAFE AS A SHORT-CUT BEFORE WE'RE ON THE MENU!
JA – THERE MUST ONLY BE A DOZEN SQUARE MILES LEFT IN OUR HANDS – AND IT'S NOT ONLY THE RUSSIANS WE'VE GOT TO WATCH OUT FOR!
HELLMAN GLANCED AT THE FIFTH TANK SEAT, NOW EMPTY...
A NAZI SNIPER'S STALKING US! HE HIT OUR POOR GUNLOADER, HEILER! HE'S SOMEWHERE ABOVE... BUT HE WON'T CATCH US WITH OUR HATCHES OPEN!
SURE ENOUGH, ABOVE...
I WANT YOUR HEAD, HELLMAN! JUST ONE SECOND'S ALL I NEED! I'LL KEEP TRACKING YOU TILL YOU OPEN YOUR COMMAND-HATCH. YOU'RE A MORE IMPORTANT 'KILL' TO ME THAN THOSE IGNORANT RUSSIAN PEASANTS!
VIKING -- A TOP-SCORING SNIPER FROM THE WAFFEN SS, HAD BEEN SET ONTO HELLMAN BY HELLMAN'S MOST BITTER ENEMY, A TOP NAZI NAMED GAULIETER KASTNER...
BUT HELLMAN'S PANTHER STAYED UNDER COVER UNTIL, AS THEY SMASHED THROUGH A DEPARTMENT STORE...
AIEEEE!
HEY – RUSSIANS SPRAYIN' THE STREETS AN' STOPPIN' THOSE CIVILIANS GETTIN' TO SHELTER!
THEY SHOULD PICK ON SOMEONE THEIR OWN SIZE!
PANTHER SIZE! YOU GOT TROUBLE IN STORE, COMRADES!
AIEEEE!

HELLMAN'S PANTHER SWUNG ACROSS THE FRONT OF THE CIVILIANS...
OKAY, WE'RE SHIELDING YOU – INTO THAT SHELTER!
DANKE, DANKE, GERMAN SOLDIER!
ABOVE...
HIMMEL – CLOSED HATCHES AGAIN! BUT YOU'RE STUPID AND SOFT ENOUGH TO THINK OF HELPING CIVILIAN SCUM, HEIN? I KNOW A WAY TO GET YOUR HEAD IN MY SIGHTS!
LESS THAN SIX MILES AWAY IN THE CHANCELLERY RUINS, THE MAN WHO HAD SET VIKING ONTO HELLMAN WAS WATCHING THROUGH THE OBSERVATORY'S TELESCOPE...
HELLMAN IS STILL ALIVE AND GETTING CLOSER! HE MUST NOT REACH ME! VIKING – WHAT ARE YOU DOING?
MOMENTS LATER...
LOOK, SIR – AN OLD WOMAN AT THAT WINDOW! THE OLD CRONE'S TOO SCARED TO MOVE! LET'S GIVE HER A HAND!
OKAY – BUT MAKE IT FAST AND KEEP YOUR EYES PEELED FOR THAT SNIPER!
HILFE, HILFE!
YOU WON'T SEE HIM, HELLMAN! I'M HERE, DISGUISED AS AN OLD WOMAN! JUST COME A LITTLE CLOSER!
OKAY, GRANDMA – COME DOWN THE STEPS!
IT – IT'S DIFFICULT... NEED MY WALKING STICK...
NOW I'VE GOT YOU, HELLMAN – I CAN GET YOU FROM THE HIP!
WAIT – THAT'S NO WALKING STICK, SIR!
KESSEL FLUNG HIS CRUTCH WITH ALL HIS MIGHT, BUT...
IT'S THE SNIPER! WATCH OUT, SIR – YAHHHHHH!
KESSEL!
MAX – DEKKER, GET HIM!
VIKING FIRED AGAIN AND AGAIN...
SO, DRESSED UP LIKE GRANNY – IN THE 'BIG, BAD WOLF', HEIN?
LET'S GET HIM, MAX!
AN' JUST LIKE THE STORY – I'M GONNA BLOW YOUR HOUSE DOWN!
GOTT – AIEEEEEEEEEE!
KESSEL... YOU SAVED MY LIFE!
ACH, ABOUT TIME, SIR! BUT I'M FINISHED WITH THE RUSSIAN FRONT! GOOD LUCK, WHATEVER HAPPENS, SIR!

SERGEANT KESSEL'S DEAD!
JUST WHEN MAX AN' ME HAD GOT USED TO HIM!
JA – THAT CRIPPLE HAD A LOT OF GUTS! AT LEAST WE SAW TO HIS KILLER!

NOW OFF, SCUM – YOU'RE DIRTYING MY TANK!
HERR KASTNER...
HEAR THAT MAGIC NAME, SIR?

KASTNER... OUR FRIEND THE GAULIETER GOT HIM ONTO US... NOW WE'RE ONLY A FEW STREETS FROM HIM! WE SHOULD MEET HIM BY MORNING!
WE CAN'T WAIT, SIR! OUR PANTHER'S DYING TO TASTE HIS BLOOD!

BUT IN THE CHANCELLERY, KASTNER AND OTHER NAZIS WERE MAKING THEIR OWN PLANS...
HE HAS DECIDED! THE FUHRER IS GOING TO SHOOT HIMSELF TONIGHT, BEFORE BERLIN FALLS!
THANK GOD! NOW WE CAN ALL MOVE! ARRANGEMENTS ARE ALL MADE! OUR PASSPORTS ARE IN ORDER – AND THE CARS ARE READY!
THE RUSSIANS ARE TWO STREETS AWAY – WE MUST MOVE QUICKLY!

AT DUSK, KASTNER LOOKED INTO THE FIRE-LIT STREETS...
WE'RE GOING, HELLMAN! BERLIN WON'T LAST ANOTHER DAY! YOU'RE DAMNED!
HERR KASTNER, WE MUST GET INTO THE CARS!

HELLMAN YELLED TO A VOLKSSTURM MAN...
TEMPLEHOF FLUGPLATZ 1KM
TEMPLEHOF, SIR... WE'VE BEEN TOLD TO MAKE A LAST STAND ROUND TEMPLEHOF AIRPORT!
OF COURSE... THE CITY AIRPORT – RIGHT NEXT TO THE CHANCELLERY! I KNOW WHAT KASTNER'S DOING!

WITH THAT SAME DUSK -- HELLMAN AND HIS CREW HAD BEEN IN THE THICK OF THE STREET FIGHTING – FALLING SLOWLY BACK...
WE'VE LOST THIS STREET TOO! HEY – THOSE VOLKSSTURM WE WERE FIGHTING WITH... THEY'RE FALLING BACK TO REGROUP!

THAT MOMENT...
GUT, THE AIRPORT ROAD WAS KEPT OPEN FOR US BY THOSE HOME GUARD FOOLS!
WE'LL MAKE THE LAST FLIGHT! WE'LL BE OUT OF THIS BERLIN HELL AND BE IN SUNNY BARCELONA BY MORNING!

BUT...
THE RUSSKIES ARE RIGHT ON US, MAJOR! KEEP REVERSIN' AS WE FIGHT?
REVERSING – RIGHT BACK TO THE AIRFIELD! WE'RE GOING TO STOP KASTNER AND HIS NAZI GANG GETTING OUT... THEY'RE STAYING HERE IN HELL WITH THE REST OF US!

THE BATTLE FOR BERLIN DRAWS TO ITS CLIMAX NEXT WEEK! DON'T MISS IT!

HELLMAN'S WAR COMES TO A FIGHTING END!
HELLMAN
ON THE RUSSIAN FRONT
APRIL 30th, 1945 – THE LAST NIGHT OF THE BATTLE OF BERLIN. FROM ALL SIDES THE RED ARMIES CLOSE IN THROUGH THE SHATTERED STREETS FOR THE CITY CENTRE. . .AND IN THAT CENTRE IS PANZER MAJOR KURT HELLMAN, READY TO FINISH THE FIGHT WITH THE RUSSIANS. . .BUT NOT BEFORE HE'S WON HIS OWN PRIVATE WAR!
A FEW HOURS LEFT THEN IT'LL BE ALL OVER! BUT WE MUST MAKE SURE KASTNER AND HIS GESTAPO CRONIES DON'T FLY OUT OF HERE! THEY STAY TO STEW IN THE JUICE LIKE THE REST OF US!
LEFT WITH HELLMAN IN THE PANTHER TANK WERE HIS TWO EX-CONVICT TANKMEN, BIG MAX AND DEKKER.
Templehof
LET'S HAVE SOME MUSIC WHILE WE WORK FROM THE AMERIKANER RADIO STATION!
HI, THERE – THIS IS AMERICAN FORCES NETWORK ON THE ELBE. OUR FIRST RECORD TONIGHT IS DEDICATED TO ALL THE NAZI BIG SHOTS. . .TITLED 'THE PARTY'S OVER'!
JA, YANK – BUT SOME OF THOSE NAZIS ARE CLEVER ENOUGH TO TRY AND LEAVE EARLY! LET'S FIGHT OUR WAY THROUGH FOR THE AIRPORT!
SURE ENOUGH, ON THE FAR SIDE OF THE STILL-INTACT CITY AIRFIELD, TWO CARLOADS OF HIGH-RANKING NAZIS HAD ARRIVED – AMONG THEM GAULIETER KASTNER, THE MAN HELLMAN HAD CARRIED ON A PRIVATE BLOOD FUED AGAINST THROUGHOUT MOST OF THE WAR!
THERE IT IS – LAST PLANE OUT LAID ON FOR US! WE'LL BE IN SUNNY SPAIN BY MORNING!
JA, AND THOSE HOME-GUARD FOOLS BUY TIME FOR US BY FIGHTING FOR THE AIRFIELD!
BUT –
THAT HOME-GUARD SERGEANT IS SUSPICIOUS!
I'M GAULIETER KASTNER AND WE'RE ON A MISSION FOR THE FUHRER!
MISSION FOR THE FUHRER, MY FOOT! YOU'RE RUNNING LIKE RATS! ALL OUT OF THAT PLANE!
SUDDENLY, HIDDEN MACHINE-GUNS BUILT INTO THE JUNKERS, OPENED UP!
AIEEEEE!
THAT'S DEALT WITH THE SCUM! NOTHING STOPS US NOW!

NEARBY –
IT'S NO GOOD, MAJOR – REDS COMIN' IN ON ALL SIDES LIKE A WALL!
NOW LET'S HAVE ONE OF THE OLD BIG-BAND NUMBERS. . .COUNT BASIE'S 'ONE O'CLOCK JUMP'!
ACH – BETTER SWITCH IT OFF NOW. WE'RE SIGNIN' OUT ANYWAY!
NO, WAIT. . .
SEE THAT SMASHED ROOF – IT'S LIKE A RAMP!
I READ YOU, MAJOR! C'MON, BIG CAT . . . WE'RE RACING STRAIGHT FOR IT!
AND –
YAAAAAH – WE'VE DONE IT! WE'RE DOING OUR OWN 'ONE O'CLOCK JUMP'! NOW ON FOR THE AIRFIELD!
AIEEEEEE!
WE'VE TAKEN A STRAY ROUND IN THE ENGINE ! WE'RE BREWIN' UP– BUT WE'RE ON THE TARMAC !
AND THAT JUNKERS PREPARING TO TAKE-OFF. . .I'LL BET KASTNER'S ON BOARD!
HIMMEL. . .SOMETHING AHEAD ON THE RUNWAY, HERR KASTNER! A-A BURNING GERMAN PANTHER!
TAKE OFF NOW, PILOT! TAKE-OFF, I SAID!
AND NOW AN AFN DEDICATION TO OUR FIGHTIN' COUSINS... THE JOCKS OF THE HIGHLAND DIVISIONS UP THERE ON THE UPPER ELBE. IT'S 'WILL YE NO' COME BACK AGAIN'!
DON'T WORRY, RADIOMAN. . . THOSE RATS AREN'T GOING ANYWHERE!
IT'S HELLMAN! THE FOOL MEANS TO KILL US ALL!
TOO LATE! TOO LATE!
AND THE NEXT RECORD WILL BE 'JUST IN TIME'!
DON'T WORRY – I DID IT IN TIME, YANK! JUMP, MAX AND DEKKER!

HELMAIEEEEEEEEEE!

MOMENTS LATER, RUSSIAN TROOPS FOUND THE CARNAGE...

THOSE GERMAN TANKMEN... SEE IF THEY ARE STILL ALIVE!

LATER–

GOTT...I'VE BEEN OUT FOR AGES! WHERE – WHERE AM I?

IN AN OFFICERS' CAGE IN THE BERLIN RUBBLE, PANZER MAJOR! YOU WERE FOUND BY THE REDS–AND YOU'RE LUCKY TO BE ALIVE!

DO YOU HEAR THE SILENCE...THE WAR IS OVER!

JA. I'VE BEEN SO USED TO THE SOUND OF GUNS AND THE GRUNTS OF BIG MAX AND DEKKER BESIDE ME... MAX AND DEKKER!

MY TWO SIDE-MEN! WHAT HAPPENED TO THEM?

ENLISTED MEN,WERE THEY? THERE'S NOT MUCH HOPE FOR THEM...

MAX AND DEKKER... EVEN THEIR CONVICT-CUNNING DIDN'T GET THEM OUT OF IT THIS TIME!

WATCH OUT – TWO PRISONER GENERALS COMING!

AND–

MEIN GOTT – MAX AND DEKKER – IN DISGUISE!

LIKE THE OUTFITS, MAJOR? THE RUSSIANS STUCK US IN A RUINED TAILOR-SHOP FOR THE NIGHT.

JA. WE FOUND THESE AND SLIPPED OUT AND SURRENDERED TO SOME OTHERS!

COULDN'T LEAVE YOU TO FEND FOR YOURSELF AFTER ALL THE FIGHTIN' WE'VE DONE TOGETHER!

AN' WEARIN' THESE MIGHT GET US BETTER TREATMENT IN THE SIBERIAN MINES!

HELLMAN TURNED TO LOOK EAST...

WE'VE LOST THE WAR AND WE'RE PRISONERS OF THE RUSSIANS! THE TIME AHEAD WILL BE HARD, BUT WITH YOUR TWO BEST FRIENDS WITH YOU, YOU HAVEN'T LOST ALL HOPE, KURT HELLMAN.

THE END

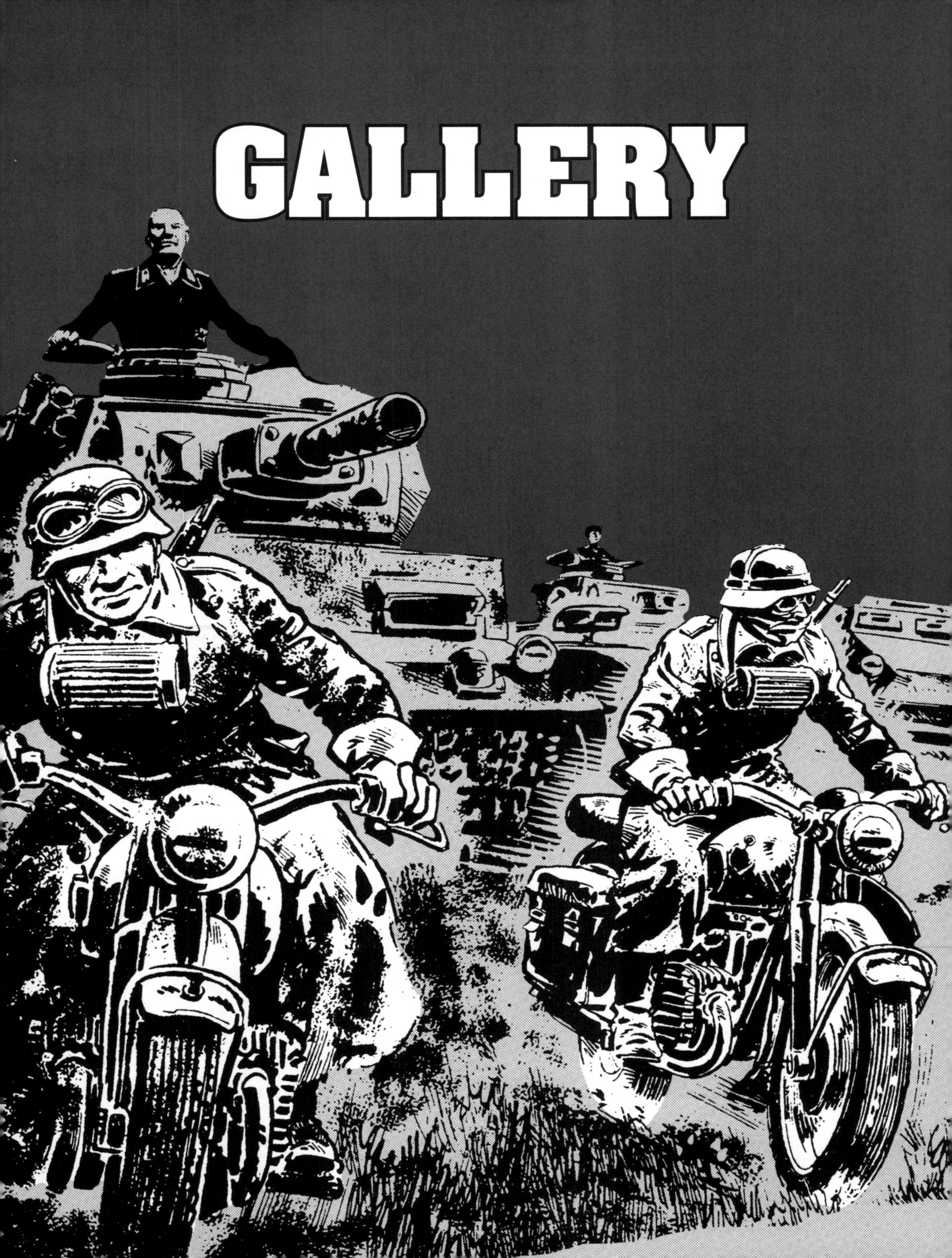
GALLERY

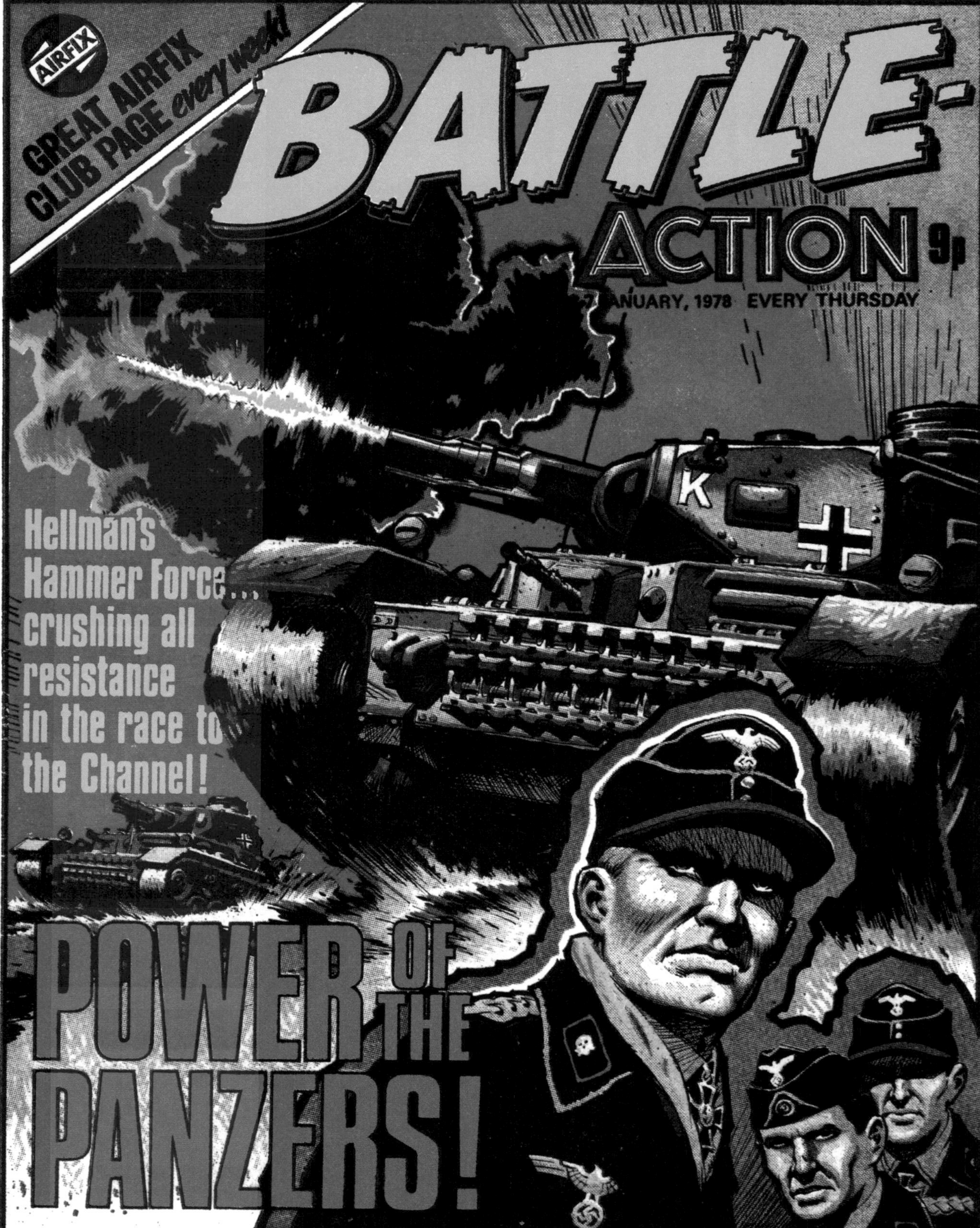
AIRFIX
GREAT AIRFIX CLUB PAGE every week!
BATTLE-
ACTION
9p
7 ANUARY, 1978 EVERY THURSDAY
K
Hellman's Hammer Force... crushing all resistance in the race to the Channel!
POWER OF THE PANZERS!
© IPC Magazines Ltd., 1978
South Africa 30c., Australia 30c., New Zealand 30c., Malaysia $1.00., Spain 20pts.

7th January 1978 Cover art by **Ian Kennedy**

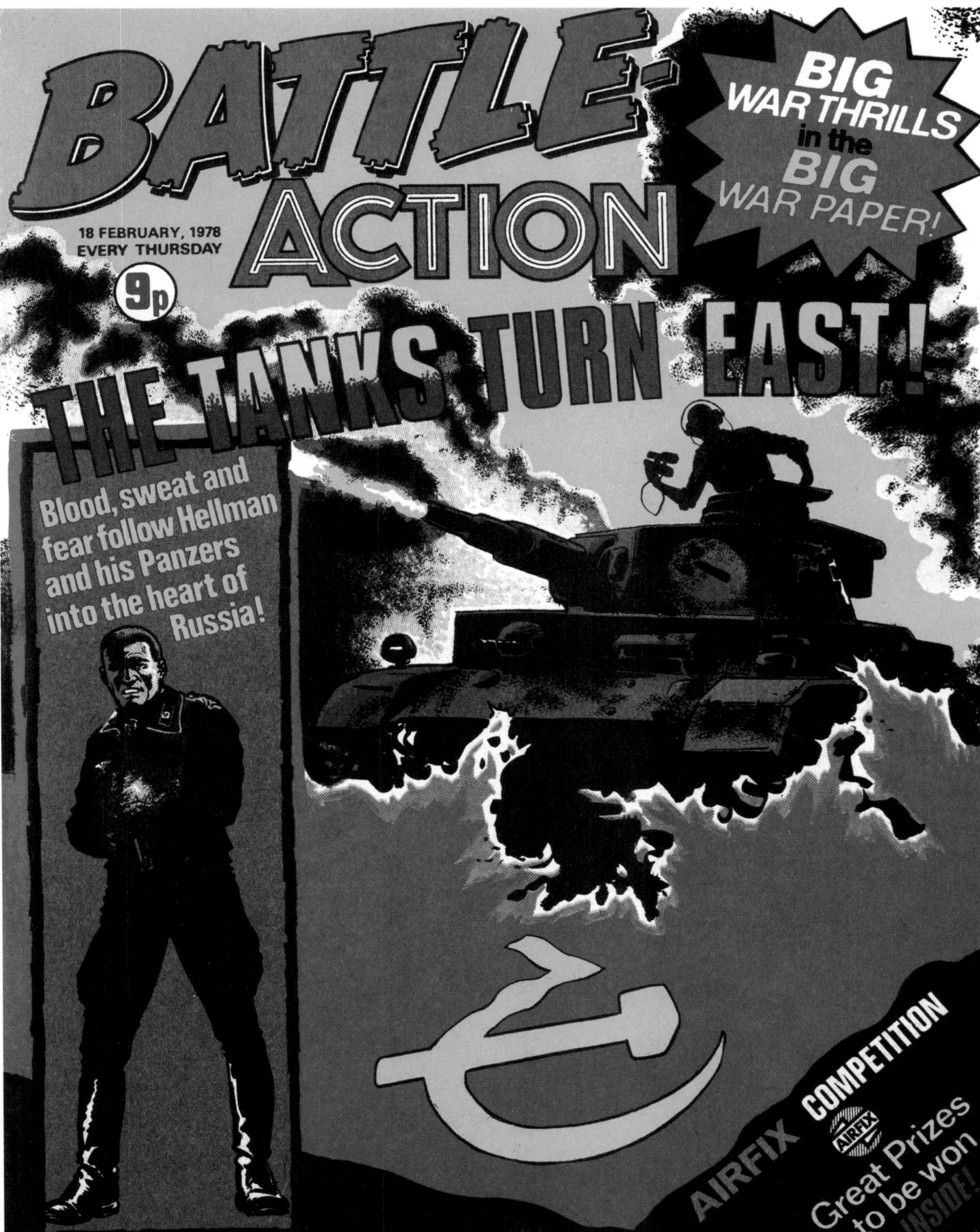
BATTLE-ACTION
18 FEBRUARY, 1978
EVERY THURSDAY
9p
BIG WAR THRILLS in the BIG WAR PAPER!
THE TANKS TURN EAST!
Blood, sweat and fear follow Hellman and his Panzers into the heart of Russia!
AIRFIX COMPETITION
AIRFIX
Great Prizes to be won INSIDE!
© IPC Magazines Ltd., 1978
South Africa 30c., Australia 30c., New Zealand 30c., Malaysia $1.00., Spain 20pts.

18th February 1978 Cover art by **Mike Dorey**

13 MAY, 1978
EVERY THURSDAY
BATTLE-ACTION
9p
A man fighting desperately to stop the Red Army...
HELLMAN
THERE'S ANOTHER GREAT AIRFIX COMPETITION in this issue!
© IPC Magazines Ltd., 1978
South Africa 30c., Australia 30c., New Zealand 30c., Malaysia $1.00., Spain 20pts.

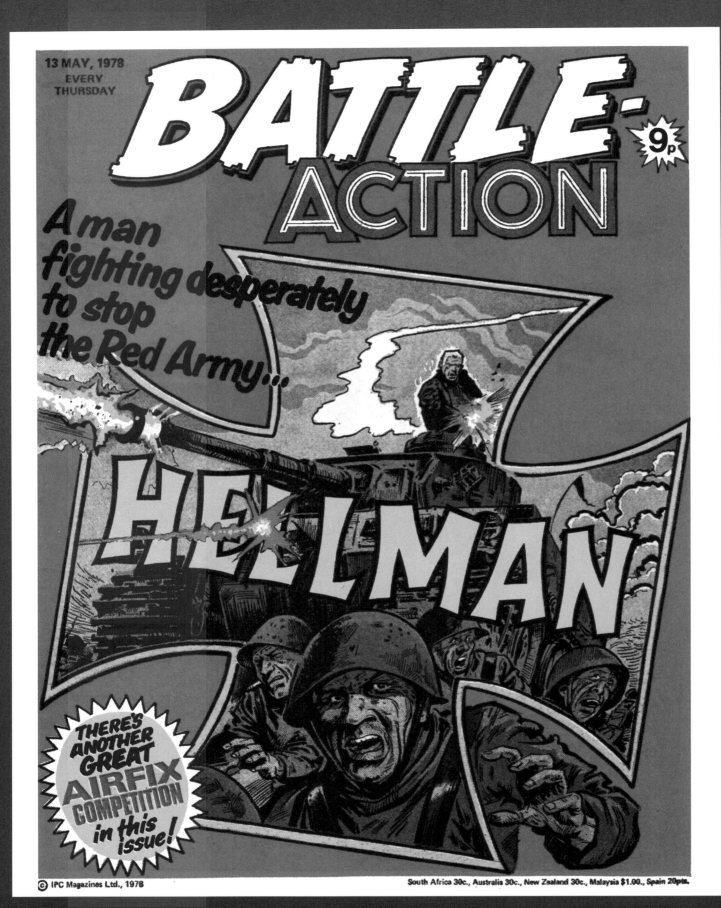

13th May 1978 Cover art by **Eric Bradbury**

BATTLE
ACTION
9p
24 JUNE, 1978
EVERY THURSDAY
The Fuhrer's funeral pyre awaits him.
The beaten German people cower in their cellars as the enemy close in! But one man fights on...
READ HELLMAN IN
BERLIN IS BURNING
© IPC Magazines Ltd., 1978
South Africa 30c., Australia 30c., New Zealand 30c., Malaysia $1.00., Spain 20pts.

24th June 1978 Cover art by **Mike Dorey**

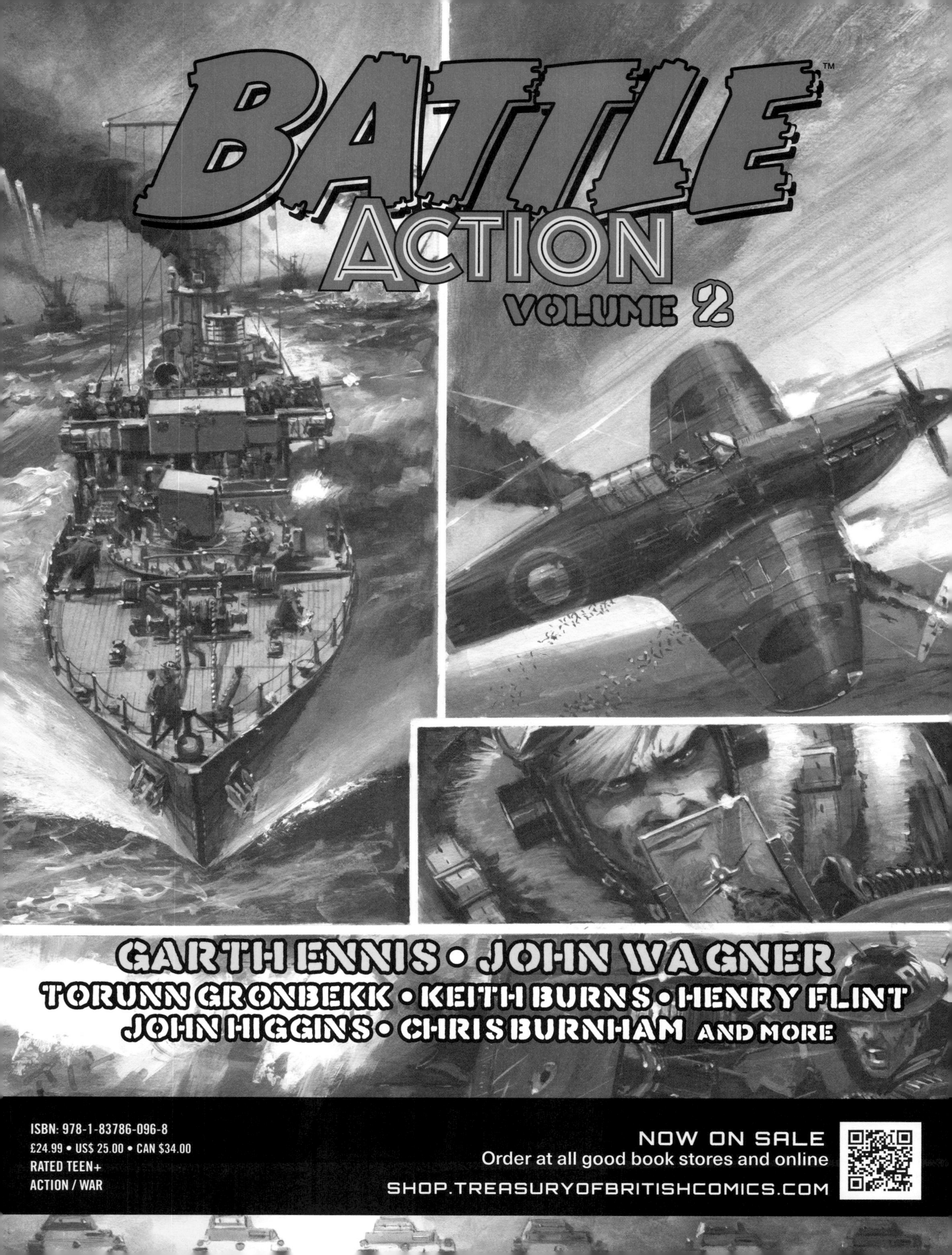

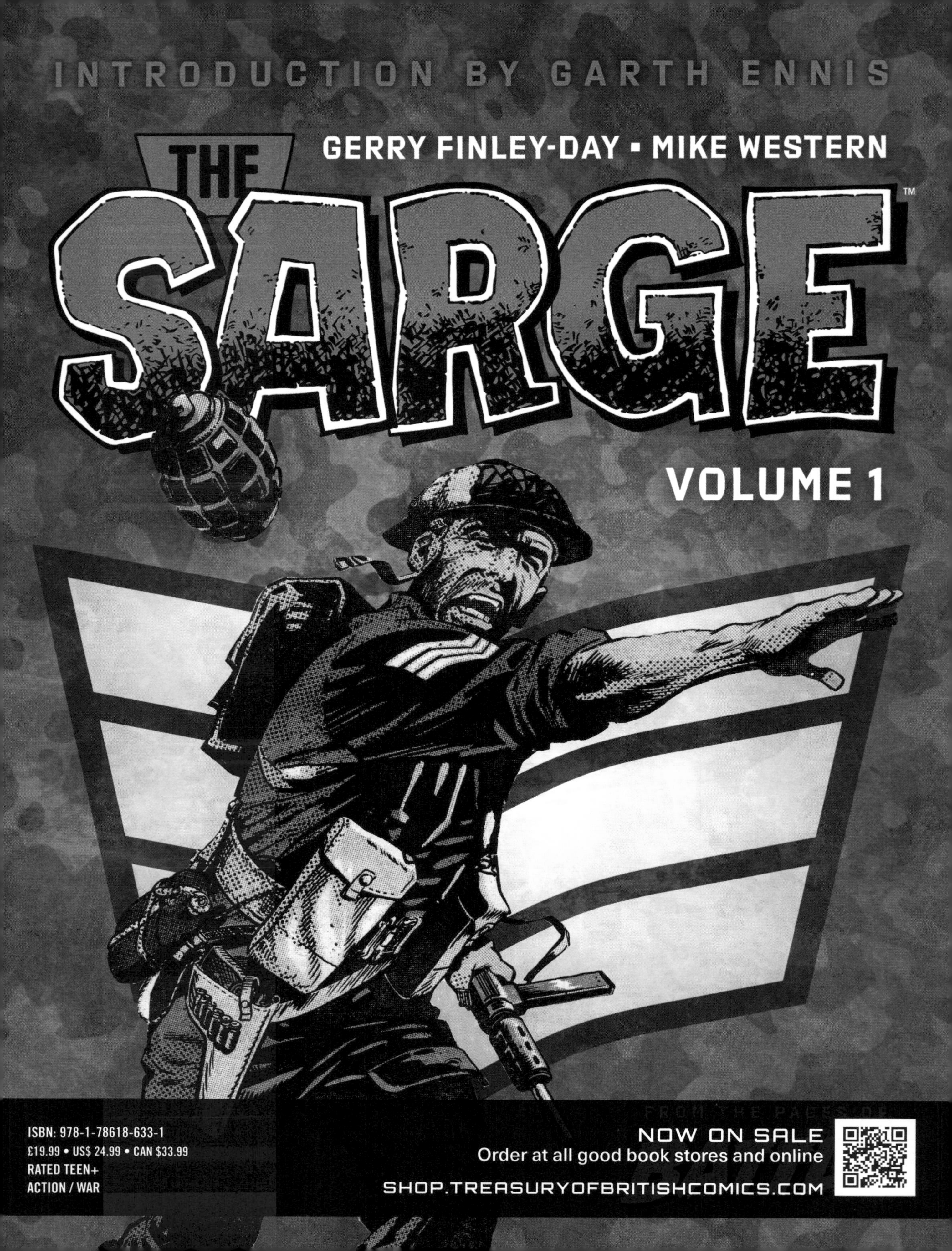